General Chemistry I

Chemistry Laboratory Manual

Tarrant County Community College - South Campus

CENGAGE
Learning™

Australia • Brazil • Japan • Korea • Mexico • Singapore • Spain • United Kingdom • United States

General Chemistry I

Executive Editor:
Michael Stranz

Managing Lab Editor:
Jeff Nunn

Custom Lab Editors:
Cooper Gouge, John Horvath

Custom Production Editor:
Jennifer Flinchpaugh

Project Coordinators:
Lisa Donahue. Peg Hagar

Senior Pre-Press Specialist:
Riley Gibb

Production Supervisor-Labs:
Melanie Evans

Rights and Permissions Specialist:
Kalina Ingham Hintz

Senior Marketing Coordinator:
Sara Mercurio

ISBN-13: 978-0-15-514687-7

ISBN-10: 0-15-514687-4

Cengage Learning
5191 Natorp Blvd.
Mason, OH 45040
USA

Cengage Learning is a leading provider of customized learning solutions with office locations around the globe, including Singapore, the United Kingdom, Australia, Mexico, Brazil, and Japan. Locate your local office at:
international.cengage.com/region

Cengage Learning products are represented in Canada by Nelson Education, Ltd.

Visit Signature Labs online at **signaturelabs.com**

Visit our corporate website at **cengage.com**

Printed in the United States of America

Custom Contents

THE DENSITIES OF LIQUIDS AND SOLIDS

One of the fundamental properties of any sample of matter is its density, which is its mass per unit of volume. The density of water is exactly 1.00000 g/cm³ at 4°C and is slightly less than one at room temperature (0.9970 g/cm³ at 25°C). Densities of liquids and solids range from values less than that of water to values considerably greater than that of water. Osmium metal has a density of 22.5 g/cm³ and is probably the densest material known at ordinary pressures.

In any density determination, two quantities must be determined—the mass and the volume of a given quantity of matter. The mass can easily be determined by weighing a sample of the substance on a balance. The quantity we usually think of as ''weight'' is really the mass of a substance. In the process of ''weighing'' we find the mass, taken from a standard set of masses, that experiences the same gravitational force as that experienced by the given quantity of matter we are weighing. The mass of a sample of liquid in a container can be found by taking the difference between the mass of the container plus the liquid and the mass of the empty container.

The volume of a liquid can easily be determined by means of a calibrated container. In the laboratory a graduated cylinder is often used for routine measurements of volume. Accurate measurement of liquid volume is made by using a pycnometer, which is simply a container having a precisely definable volume. The volume of a solid can be determined by direct measurement if the solid has a regular geometrical shape. Such is not usually the case, however, with ordinary solid samples. A convenient way to determine the volume of a solid is to measure accurately the volume of liquid displaced when an amount of the solid is immersed in the liquid. The volume of the solid will equal the volume of liquid which it displaces.

In this experiment we will determine the density of a liquid and a solid by the procedure we have outlined. First we weigh an empty flask and its stopper. We then fill the flask completely with water, measuring the mass of the filled stoppered flask. From the difference in these two masses we find the mass of water and then, from the known density of water, we determine the volume of the flask. We empty and dry the flask, fill it with an unknown liquid, and weigh again. From the mass of the liquid and the volume of the flask we find the density of the liquid. To determine the density of an unknown solid metal, we add the metal to the dry empty flask and weigh. This allows us to find the mass of the metal. We then fill the flask with water, leaving the metal in the flask, and weigh again. The increase in mass is that of the added water; from that increase, and the density of water, we calculate the volume of water we added. The volume of the metal must equal the volume of the flask minus the volume of water. From the mass and volume of the metal we calculate its density. The calculations involved are outlined in detail in the Advance Study Assignment.

Experimental Procedure

WEAR YOUR SAFETY GLASSES WHILE PERFORMING THIS EXPERIMENT

A. Mass of a Coin

After you have been shown how to operate the analytical balances in your laboratory, read the section on balances in Appendix IV. Take a coin and measure its mass to 0.0001 g. Record the mass on the DATA page. If your balance has a TARE bar, use it to re-zero the balance. Take

another coin and weigh it, recording its mass. Remove both coins, zero the balance, and weigh both coins together, recording the total mass. If you have no TARE bar on your balance, add the second coin and measure and record the mass of the two coins. Then remove both coins and find the mass of the second one by itself. When you are satisfied that your results are those you would expect, go to the stockroom and obtain a glass-stoppered flask, which will serve as a pycnometer, and samples of an unknown liquid and an unknown metal.

B. Density of a Liquid

If your flask is not clean and dry, clean it with soap and water, rinse it with a few cubic centimeters of acetone, and dry it by letting it stand for a few minutes in the air or by *gently* blowing compressed air into it for a few moments.

Weigh the dry flask with its stopper on the analytical balance, or the toploading balance if so directed, to the nearest milligram. Fill the flask with distilled water until the liquid level is nearly to the *top* of the ground surface in the neck. Put the stopper in the flask in order to drive out *all* the air and any excess water. Work the stopper gently into the flask, so that it is firmly seated in position. Wipe any water form the outside of the flask with a towel and soak up all excess water from around the top of the stopper.

Again weigh the flask, which should be completely dry on the outside and full of water, to the nearest milligram. Given the density of water at the temperature of the laboratory and the mass of water in the flask, you should be able to determine the volume of the flask very precisely. Empty the flask, dry it, and fill it with your unknown liquid. Stopper and dry the flask as you did when working with the water and then weigh the stoppered flask full of the unknown liquid, making sure its surface is dry. This measurement, used in conjunction with those you made previously, will allow you to find accurately the density of your unknown liquid.

C. Density of a Solid

Pour your sample of liquid from the flask into its container. Rinse the flask with a small amount of acetone and dry it thoroughly. Add small chunks of the metal sample to the flask until the flask is at least half full. Weigh the flask, with its stopper and the metal, to the nearest milligram. You should have at least 50 g of metal in the flask.

Leaving the metal in the flask, fill the flask with water and then replace the stopper. Roll the metal around in the flask to make sure that no air remains between the metal pieces. Refill the flask if necessary, and then weigh the dry, stoppered flask full of water plus the metal sample. Properly done, the measurements you have made in this experiment will allow a calculation of the density of your metal sample that will be accurate to about 0.1%.

Pour the water from the flask. Put the metal in its container. Dry the flask and return it with its stopper and your metal sample, along with the sample of unknown liquid, to the stockroom.

Experiment *Name* ______________ *Section* ______

Data and Calculations: Densities of Liquids and Solids

A. Mass of coin 1 ________ g Mass of coin 2 ________ g

Mass of coins 1 and 2 weighed together ________ g

What general law is illustrated by the results of this experiment?

B. Density of unknown liquid

Mass of empty flask plus stopper ________ g

Mass of stoppered flask plus water ________ g

Mass of stoppered flask plus liquid ________ g

Mass of water ________ g

Volume of flask (density of H_2O at 25°C, 0.9970 g/cm^3; at 20°C, 0.9982 g/cm^3) ________ cm^3

Mass of liquid ________ g

Density of liquid ________ g/cm^3

To how many significant figures can the liquid density be properly reported? (See Appendix V.) ________

C. Density of unknown metal

Mass of stoppered flask plus metal ________ g

Mass of stoppered flask plus metal plus water ________ g

Mass of metal ________ g

Mass of water ________ g

Volume of water ________ cm^3

Volume of metal ________ cm^3

(continued on following page)

(continued)

Density of metal ______ g/cm^3

To how many significant figures can the density of the metal be properly reported? ______

Explain why the value obtained for the density of the metal is likely to have a larger percentage error than that found for the liquid.

Unknown liquid no. ______ Unknown solid no. ______

Experiment *Name* ______________________ *Section* __________

Advance Study Assignment: Densities of Solids and Liquids

The advance study assignments in this laboratory manual are designed to assist you in making the calculations required in the experiment you will be doing. We do this by furnishing you with sample data and showing in some detail how that data can be used to obtain the desired results. In the advance study assignments we will often include the guiding principles as well as the specific relationships to be employed. If you work through the steps in each calculation by yourself, you should have no difficulty when you are called upon to make the necessary calculations on the basis of the data you obtain in the laboratory.

1. *Finding the volume of a flask.* A student obtained a clean, dry glass-stoppered flask. She weighed the flask and stopper on an analytical balance and found the total mass to be 32.634 g. She then filled the flask with water and obtained a mass for the full stoppered flask of 59.479 g. From these data, and the fact that at the temperature of the laboratory the density of water was 0.9973 g/cm^3, find the volume of the stoppered flask.

a. First we need to obtain the mass of the water in the flask. This is found by recognizing that the mass of a sample is equal to the sum of the masses of its parts. For the filled stoppered flask:

Mass of filled stoppered flask = mass of empty stoppered flask + mass of water,
so mass of water = mass of filled flask − mass of empty flask

Mass of water = __________ g − __________ g = __________ g

Many mass and volume measurements in chemistry are made by the method used in 1a. This method is called measuring by difference, and is a very useful one.

b. The density of a pure substance is equal to its mass divided by its volume:

$$\text{Density} = \frac{\text{mass}}{\text{volume}} \quad \text{or} \quad \text{volume} = \frac{\text{mass}}{\text{density}}$$

The volume of the flask is equal to the volume of the water it contains. Since we know the mass and density of the water, we can find its volume and that of the flask. Make the necessary calculation.

Volume of water = volume of flask = __________ cm^3

2. *Finding the density of an unknown liquid.* Having obtained the volume of the flask, the student emptied the flask, dried it, and filled it with an unknown whose density she wished to determine. The mass of the stoppered flask when completely filled with liquid was 50.376 g. Find the density of the liquid.

a. First we need to find the mass of the liquid by measuring by difference:

Mass of liquid = __________ g − __________ g = __________ g

(continued on following page)

(continued)

b. Since the volume of the liquid equals that of the flask, we know both the mass and volume of the liquid and can easily find its density using the equation in 1b. Make the calculation.

Density of liquid = ____________ g/cm^3

3. *Finding the density of a solid.* The student then emptied the flask and dried it once again. To the empty flask she added pieces of a metal until the flask was about half full. She weighed the stoppered flask and its metal contents and found that the mass was 152.047 g. She then filled the flask with water, stoppered it, and obtained a total mass of 165.541 g for the flask, stopper, metal, and water. Find the density of the metal.

a. To find the density of the metal we need to know its mass and volume. We can easily obtain its mass by the method of differences:

Mass of metal = ____________ g − ____________ g = ____________ g

b. To determine the volume of metal, we note that the volume of the flask must equal the volume of the metal plus the volume of water in the filled flask containing both metal and water. If we can find the volume of water, we can obtain the volume of metal by the method of differences. To obtain the volume of the water we first calculate its mass:

Mass of water = mass of (flask + stopper + metal + water)
− mass of (flask + stopper + metal)

Mass of water = ____________ g − ____________ g = ____________ g

The volume of water is found from its density, as in 1b. Make the calculation.

Volume of water = ____________ cm^3

c. From the volume of the water we calculate the volume of metal:

Volume of metal = volume of flask − volume of water

Volume of metal = ____________ cm^3 − ____________ cm^3 = ____________ cm^3

From the mass of and volume of metal we find the density, using the equation in 1b. Make the calculation.

Density of metal = ____________ g/cm^3

Now go back to Question 1 and check to see that you have reported the proper number of significant figures in each of the results you calculated in this assignment. Use the rules on significant figures as given in your chemistry text or Appendix V.

DETERMINATION OF A CHEMICAL FORMULA

When atoms of one element combine with those of another, the combining ratio is typically an integer or a simple fraction; 1:2, 1:1, 2:1, and 2:3 are ratios one might encounter. The simplest formula of a compound expresses that atom ratio. Some substances with the ratios we listed include $CaCl_2$, KBr, Ag_2O, and Fe_2O_3. When more than two elements are present in a compound, the formula still indicates the atom ratio. Thus the substance with the formula Na_2SO_4 indicates that the sodium, sulfur, and oxygen atoms occur in that compound in the ratio 2:1:4. Many compounds have more complex formulas than those we have noted, but the same principles apply.

To find the formula of a compound we need to find the mass of each of the elements in a weighed sample of that compound. For example, if we resolved a sample of the compound NaOH weighing 40 grams into its elements, we would find that we obtained just about 23 grams of sodium, 16 grams of oxygen, and 1 gram of hydrogen. Since the atomic mass scale tells us that sodium atoms have a relative mass of 23, oxygen atoms a relative mass of 16, and hydrogen atoms a relative mass of just about 1, we would conclude that the sample of NaOH contained equal numbers of Na, O, and H atoms. Since that is the case, the atom ratio Na:O:H is 1:1:1, and so the simplest formula is NaOH. In terms of moles, we can say that that one mole of NaOH, 40 grams, contains one mole of Na, 23 grams, one mole of O, 16 grams, and one mole of H, 1 gram, where we define the mole to be that mass in grams equal numerically to the sum of the atomic masses in an element or a compound. From this kind of argument we can conclude that the atom ratio in a compound is equal to the mole ratio. We get the mole ratio from chemical analysis, and from that the formula of the compound.

In this experiment we will use these principles to find the formula of the compound with the general formula $Cu_xCl_y \cdot zH_2O$, where the x, y, and z are integers which, when known, establish the formula of the compound. (In expressing the formula of a compound like this one, where water molecules remain intact within the compound, we retain the formula of H_2O in the formula of the compound.)

The compound we will study, which is called copper chloride hydrate, turns out to be ideal for one's first venture into formula determination. It is stable, can be obtained in pure form, has a characteristic blue-green color which changes as the compound is changed chemically, and is relatively easy to decompose into the elements and water. In the experiment we will first drive out the water, which is called the water of hydration, from an accurately weighed sample of the compound. This occurs if we gently heat the sample to a little over 100°C. As the water is driven out, the color of the sample changes from blue-green to a tan-brown color similar to that of tobacco. The compound formed is anhydrous (no water) copper chloride. If we subtract its mass from that of the hydrate, we can determine the mass of the water that was driven off, and, using the molar mass of water, find the number of moles of H_2O that were in the sample.

In the next step we need to find either the mass of copper or the mass of chlorine in the anhydrous sample we have prepared. It turns out to be much easier to determine the mass of the copper, and find the mass of chlorine by difference. We do this by dissolving the anhydrous sample in water, which gives us a green solution containing copper and chloride ions. To that solution we add some aluminum metal wire. Aluminum is what we call an active metal; in contact with a solution containing copper ions, the aluminum metal will react chemically with those ions, converting them to copper metal. The aluminum is said to reduce the copper ions to the metal, and is itself oxidized. The copper metal appears on the wire as the reaction proceeds, and has the typical red-orange color. When the reaction is complete, we remove the excess Al, separate the copper from the solution, and weigh the dried metal. From its mass we can calculate the number of moles of copper in the sample. We find the mass of chlorine by subtracting the mass of copper from that of the anhydrous copper chloride, and from that value determine the number of moles of chlorine. The mole ratio for Cu : Cl : H_2O gives us the formula of the compound.

Experimental Procedure

WEAR YOUR SAFETY GLASSES WHILE PERFORMING THIS EXPERIMENT 

Weigh a clean, dry crucible, without a cover, accurately on the analytical balance. Place about 1 gram of the unknown hydrated copper chloride in the crucible. With your spatula, break up any sizeable crystal particles by pressing them against the wall of the crucible. Then weigh the crucible and its contents accurately. Enter your results on the DATA page.

Place the uncovered crucible on a clay triangle supported by an iron ring. Light your bunsen burner away from the crucible, and adjust the burner so that you have a small flame. Holding the burner in your hand, gently heat the crucible as you move the burner back and forth. Do not overheat the sample. As the sample warms, you will see that the green crystals begin to change to brown around the edges. Continue gentle heating, slowly converting all of the hydrated crystals to the anhydrous brown form. After all of the crystals appear to be brown, continue heating gently, moving the burner back and forth judiciously, for an additional two minutes. Remove the burner, cover the crucible to minimize rehydration, and let it cool for about 15 minutes. Remove the cover, and slowly roll the brown crystals around the crucible. If some green crystals remain, repeat the heating process. Finally, weigh the cool uncovered crucible and its contents accurately.

Transfer the brown crystals in the crucible to an empty 50-mL beaker. Rinse out the crucible with two 5- to 7-mL portions of distilled water, and add the rinsings to the beaker. Swirl the beaker gently to dissolve the brown solid. The color will change to green as the copper ions are rehydrated. Measure out about 20 cm of 20-gauge aluminum wire ($\sim$0.25 g) and form the wire into a loose spiral coil. Put the coil into the solution so that it is completely immersed. Within a few moments you will observe some evolution of H_2, hydrogen gas, and the formation of copper metal on the Al wire. As the copper ions are reduced, the color of the solution will fade. The Al metal wire will be slowly oxidized and enter the solution as aluminum ions.

When the reaction is complete, which will take about 30 minutes, the solution will be colorless, and most of the copper metal that was produced will be on the Al wire. Add 5 drops of 6 M HCl to dissolve any insoluble aluminum salts and clear up the solution. Use your glass stirring rod to remove the copper from the wire as completely as you can. Slide the unreacted aluminum wire up the wall of the beaker with your stirring rod, and, while the wire is hanging from the rod, rinse off any remaining Cu particles with water from your wash bottle. If necessary, complete the removal of the Cu with a drop or two of 6 M HCl added directly to the wire. Put the wire aside; it has done its duty.

In the beaker you now have the metallic copper produced in the reaction, in a solution containing an aluminum salt. Set up a small Buchner funnel fitted with a moistened piece of filter paper. With light suction, decant the solution into the funnel. (Don't worry if some of the copper is also transferred.) Wash the copper metal in the beaker with small portions of distilled water; decant the wash into the funnel. Break up any copper particles with your stirring rod, and wash again, twice. Transfer the wash and the copper to the filter funnel. Wash any remaining copper into the funnel with water from your wash bottle. *All* of the copper must be transferred to the funnel. Rinse the copper on the paper once again with water. Turn off the suction. Add 10 mL of 95% ethanol to the funnel, and after a minute or so turn on the suction. Draw air through the funnel for about 5 minutes. Transfer the copper from the funnel to a weighed watch glass; this is perhaps most easily done by lifting the edge of the filter paper with a spatula and then lifting the paper from the funnel. The transfer must be quantitative; scrape any copper that adheres to the paper on to the watch glass with your spatula. Dry the copper on the watch glass under a heat lamp for 5 minutes. Allow to cool to room temperature and then weigh accurately.

Dispose of the liquid waste and copper produced in the experiment as directed by your instructor.

Experiment *Name* ______________________ *Section* __________

Data and Calculations: Determination of a Chemical Formula

Atomic masses: Copper __________ Cl __________ H __________ O __________

Mass of crucible __________ g

Mass of crucible and hydrated sample __________ g

Mass of hydrated sample __________ g

Mass of crucible and dehydrated sample __________ g

Mass of dehydrated sample __________ g

Mass of empty watch glass __________ g

Mass of watch glass and copper __________ g

Mass of copper __________ g

No. moles of copper __________ moles

Mass of water evolved __________ g

No. moles of water __________ moles

Mass of chlorine in sample (by difference) __________ g

No. moles of chlorine __________ moles

Mole ratio, chlorine : copper in sample __________ : 1

Mole ratio, water : copper in hydrated sample __________ : 1

Formula of dehydrated sample (round to nearest integer) __________

Formula of hydrated sample __________

Experiment *Name* ____________________ *Section* __________

Advance Study Assignment: Determination of a Chemical Formula

1. To find the mass of a mole of an element, one looks up the atomic mass of the element in a table of atomic masses (see Appendix III or the Periodic Table). The molar mass of an element is simply the mass in grams of that element that is numerically equal to its atomic mass. For a compound substance, the molar mass is equal to the mass in grams that is numerically equal to the sum of the atomic masses in the formula of the substance. Find the molar mass of

Cu ______ g Cl ______ g H ______ g O ______ g H_2O ______ g

2. If one can find the ratio of the number of moles of the elements in a compound to one another, one can find the formula of the compound. In a certain compound of copper and oxygen, Cu_xO_y, we find that a sample weighing 0.5424 g contains 0.4831 g Cu.

a. How many moles of Cu are there in the sample?

$$\left(\text{No. moles} = \frac{\text{mass Cu}}{\text{molar mass Cu}}\right)$$

__________ moles

b. How many grams of O are there in the sample? (The mass of the sample equals the mass of Cu plus the mass of O.)

__________ g

c. How many moles of O are there in the sample?

__________ moles

d. What is the mole ratio (no. moles Cu/no. moles O) in the sample?

__________ : 1

e. What is the formula of the oxide? (The atom ratio equals the mole ratio, and is expressed using the smallest integers possible.)

____

f. What is the molar mass of the copper oxide?

__________ g

Experiment

Properties of Hydrates

Most solid chemical compounds will contain some water if they have been exposed to the atmosphere for any length of time. In most cases the water is present in very small amounts, and is merely adsorbed on the surface of the crystals. Other solid compounds contain larger amounts of water that is chemically bound in the crystal. These compounds are usually ionic salts. The water that is present in these salts is called water of hydration and is usually bound to the cations in the salt.

The water molecules in a hydrate are removed relatively easily. In many cases, simply heating a hydrate to a temperature somewhat above the boiling point of water will drive off the water of hydration. Hydrated barium chloride is typical in this regard; it is converted to anhydrous $BaCl_2$ if heated to about 115°C:

$$BaCl_2 \cdot 2H_2O(s) \longrightarrow BaCl_2(s) + 2\ H_2O(g) \text{ at } t \geq 115°C$$

In the dehydration reaction the crystal structure of the solid will change, and the color of the salt may also change. In Experiment 4, when copper chloride hydrate was gently heated, it was converted to the brownish anhydride.

Some hydrates lose water to the atmosphere upon standing in air. This process is called efflorescence. The amount of water lost depends on the amount of water in the air, as measured by its relative humidity, and the temperature. In moist warm air, $CoCl_2$ is fully hydrated and exists as $CoCl_2 \cdot 6H_2O$, which is red. In cold dry air the salt loses most of its water of hydration and is found as anhydrous $CoCl_2$, which is blue. At intermediate humidities and 25°C, we find the stable form is the violet dihydrate, $CoCl_2 \cdot 2H_2O$. In the old days one could obtain inexpensive hygrometers that indicated the humidity by the color of the cobalt chloride they contained.

Some anhydrous ionic compounds will tend to absorb water from the air or other sources so strongly that they can be used to dry liquids or gases. These substances are called desiccants, and are said to be hygroscopic. A few ionic compounds can take up so much water from the air that they dissolve in the water they absorb; sodium hydroxide, NaOH, will do this. This process is called deliquescence.

Some compounds evolve water on being heated but are not true hydrates. The water is produced by decomposition of the compound rather than by loss of water of hydration. Organic compounds, particularly carbohydrates, behave this way. Decompositions of this sort are not reversible; adding water to the product will not regenerate the original compound. True hydrates typically undergo reversible dehydration. Adding water to anhydrous $BaCl_2$ will cause formation of $BaCl_2 \cdot 2H_2O$, or if enough water is added you will get a solution containing Ba^{2+} and Cl^- ions. Many ionic hydrates are soluble in water, and are usually prepared by crystallization from water solution. If you order barium chloride from a chemical supply house, you will probably get crystals of $BaCl_2 \cdot 2H_2O$, which is a stable, stoichiometrically pure, compound. The amount of bound water may depend on the way the hydrate is prepared, but in general the number of moles of water per mole of compound is either an integer or a multiple of ½.

In this experiment you will study some of the properties of hydrates. You will identify the hydrates in a group of compounds, observe the reversibility of the hydration reaction, and test some substances for efflorescence or deliquescence. Finally you will be asked to determine the amount of water lost by a sample of unknown hydrate on heating. From this amount, if given the formula or the molar mass of the anhydrous sample, you will be able to calculate the formula of the hydrate itself.

Experimental Procedure

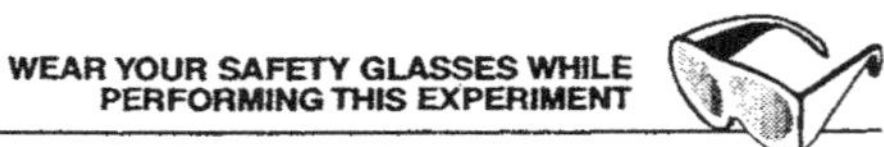

WEAR YOUR SAFETY GLASSES WHILE
PERFORMING THIS EXPERIMENT

A. Identification of Hydrates

Place about 0.5 g of each of the compounds listed below in small, dry test tubes, one compound to a tube. Observe carefully the behavior of each compound when you heat it gently with a burner flame. If droplets of water condense on the cool upper walls of the test tube, this is evidence that the compound may be a hydrate. Note the nature and color of the residue. Let the tube cool and try to dissolve the residue in a few cm^3 of water, warming very gently if necessary. A true hydrate will tend to dissolve in water, producing a solution with a color very similar to that of the original hydrate. If the compound is a carbohydrate, it will give off water on heating and will tend to char. The solution of the residue in water will often be caramel colored.

Nickel chloride	Sucrose
Potassium chloride	Calcium carbonate
Sodium tetraborate (borax)	Barium chloride

B. Reversibility of Hydration

Gently heat a few crystals, ~0.3 g, of hydrated cobalt(II) chloride, $CoCl_2 \cdot 6\,H_2O$, in an evaporating dish until the color change appears to be complete. Dissolve the residue in the evaporating dish in a few cm^3 of water from your wash bottle. Heat the resulting solution to boiling **CAUTION**, and carefully boil it to dryness. Note any color changes. Put the evaporating dish on the lab bench and let it cool.

C. Deliquescence and Efflorescence

Place a few crystals of each of the compounds listed below on separate watch glasses and put them next to the dish of $CoCl_2$ prepared in Part B. Depending on their composition and the relative humidity (amount of moisture in the air), the samples may gradually lose water of hydration to, or pick up water from, the air. They may also remain unaffected. To establish whether the samples gain or lose mass, weigh each of them on a top-loading balance to 0.01 g. Record their masses. Weigh them again after about an hour to detect any change in mass. Observe the samples occasionally during the laboratory period, noting any changes in color, crystal structure, or degree of wetness that may occur.

$Na_2CO_3 \cdot 10\,H_2O$ (washing soda)	$KAl(SO_4)_2 \cdot 12\,H_2O$ (alum)
$CaCl_2$	$CuSO_4$

D. Per Cent Water in a Hydrate

Clean a porcelain crucible and its cover with 6 M HNO_3. Any stains that are not removed by this treatment will not interfere with this experiment. Rinse the crucible and cover with distilled water. Put the crucible with its cover slightly ajar on a clay triangle and heat with a burner flame, gently at first and then to redness for about 2 minutes. Allow the crucible and cover to cool, and then weigh them to 0.001 g on an analytical balance. Handle the crucible with clean crucible tongs.

Obtain a sample of unknown hydrate from the stockroom and place about a gram of sample in the crucible. Weigh the crucible, cover, and sample on the balance. Put the crucible on the clay triangle, with the cover in an off-center position to allow the escape of water vapor. Heat again, gently at first and then strongly, keeping the bottom of the crucible at red heat for about 10 minutes. Center the cover on the crucible and let it cool to room temperature. Weigh the cooled crucible along with its cover and contents.

Examine the solid residue. Add water until the crucible is two thirds full and stir. Warm gently if the residue does not dissolve readily. Does the residue appear to be soluble in water?

DISPOSAL OF REACTION PRODUCTS. Dispose of the residues in this experiment as directed by your instructor.

Name ______________________ **Section** ____________

Experiment

Data and Calculations: Properties of Hydrates

A. Identification of Hydrates

	H_2O appears	Color of residue	Water soluble	Hydrate
Nickel chloride	______	______	______	______
Potassium chloride	______	______	______	______
Sodium tetraborate	______	______	______	______
Sucrose	______	______	______	______
Calcium carbonate	______	______	______	______
Barium chloride	______	______	______	______

B. Reversibility of Hydration

Summarize your observations on $CoCl_2 \cdot 6\ H_2O$:

Is the dehydration and hydration of $CoCl_2$ reversible?

C. Deliquescence and Efflorescence

	Mass (sample + glass)			
	Initial	Final	Observations	Conclusions
$Na_2CO_3 \cdot 10\ H_2O$	______	______	______	______
$KAl(SO_4)_2 \cdot 12\ H_2O$	______	______	______	______
$CaCl_2$	______	______	______	______
$CuSO_4$	______	______	______	______
$CoCl_2$	______	______	______	______

(continued on following page)

D. Per Cent Water in a Hydrate

Mass of crucible and cover ____________ g

Mass of crucible, cover, and solid hydrate ____________ g

Mass of crucible, cover, and residue ____________ g

Calculations and Results

Mass of solid hydrate ____________ g

Mass of residue ____________ g

Mass of H_2O lost ____________ g

Percentage of H_2O in the unknown hydrate ____________ %

Formula mass of anhydrous salt (if furnished) ____________

Number of moles of water per mole of unknown hydrate ____________

Unknown no. ____________

Name ______________________________ **Section** ______________

Experiment

Advance Study Assignment: Properties of Hydrates

1. A student is given a sample of a green nickel sulfate hydrate. She weighs the sample in a dry covered crucible and obtains a mass of 22.326 g for the crucible, cover, and sample. Earlier she had found that the crucible and cover weighed 21.244 g. She then heats the crucible to drive off the water of hydration, keeping the crucible at red heat for about 10 minutes with the cover slightly ajar. She then lets the crucible cool, and finds it has a lower mass; the crucible, cover and contents then weigh 21.840 g. In the process the sample was converted to yellow anhydrous $NiSO_4$.

   a. What was the mass of the hydrate sample?

   ______________ g hydrate

   b. What is the mass of the anhydrous $NiSO_4$?

   ______________ g $NiSO_4$

   c. How much water was driven off?

   ______________ g H_2O

   d. What is the percentage of water in the hydrate?

   $$\% \text{ water} = \frac{\text{mass of water in sample}}{\text{mass of hydrate sample}} \times 100\%$$

   ______________ % H_2O

   e. How many grams of water would there be in 100.0 g hydrate? How many moles?

   ______________ g H_2O; ______________ moles H_2O

   f. How many grams of $NiSO_4$ are there in 100.0 g hydrate? How many moles? (What percentage of the hydrate is $NiSO_4$? Convert the mass of $NiSO_4$ to moles. Molar mass of $NiSO_4$ is 154.8 g.)

   ______________ g $NiSO_4$; ______________ moles $NiSO_4$

   g. How many moles of water are present per mole $NiSO_4$?

   ____

   h. What is the formula of the hydrate?

   ____

EXPERIMENT

A Sequence of Chemical Reactions

OBJECTIVES : To study types of chemical reactions and to develop laboratory skills for carrying out quantitative chemical procedures.

CONCEPT TO BE TESTED: We can use a number of chemical reactions to convert copper from one form (compound) to another, but in the end the mass of copper should be the same.

Text References: (1) Whitten, K. W., Davis, R. E., and Peck, L. *General Chemistry,* 5th ed., Saunders College Publishing, Philadelphia, 1996, Sections 3.1-3.5 and Chapter 4. (2) Safety pp 1-7 (3) Laboratory Techniques Section A, B, E, and F.1

INTRODUCTION (Two laboratory periods required)

Chemists often use stepwise procedures involving a sequence of chemical reactions to obtain a desired product. In a sequence the available starting material changes into product over a number of steps. In this experiment you will study several types of chemical reactions by carrying a starting material, Cu(s), through a sequence of chemical steps and recovering it at the end of the experiment (Figure 1).

As you read through the Introduction, note that you can describe chemical changes by (1) molecular equations, (2) total ionic equations, and (3) net ionic equations. These are three ways to represent the same chemical reaction.

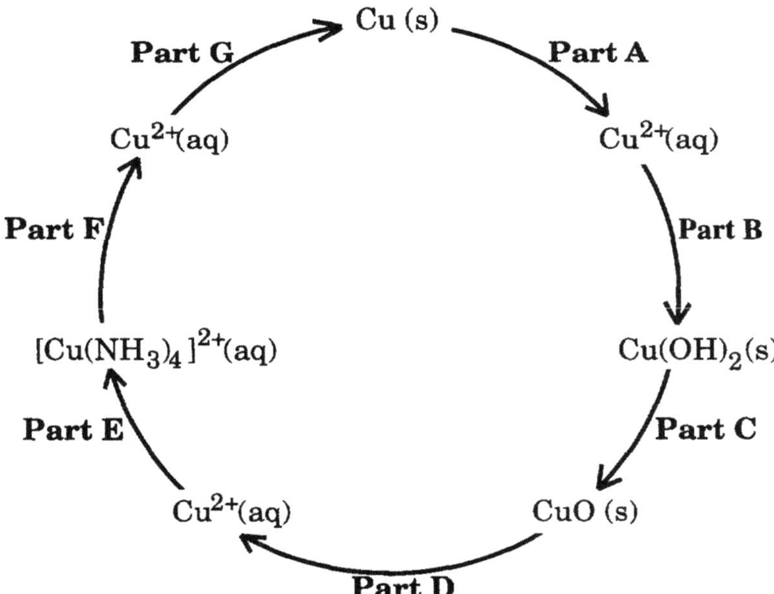

Figure 1 Sequence of chemical reactions for copper.

You will observe in Figure 1 that the sequence of chemical reactions involves different types of chemical changes and that this particular sequence of reactions leads you back to

created nor destroyed in chemical reactions, theoretically, you should recover the same mass of copper at the end of the sequence. This assumes that all steps were performed with 100% efficiency. You will test your efficiency by using the initial mass of copper to determine the % yield of CuO (optional) and % recovery of Cu.

We can group thousands of chemical reactions into just a few classes of reactions.

Combination Reactions. *Two or more substances combine to form another substance.*

Decomposition Reactions. *One compound breaks down into two or more substances.*

Metathetical or Double Displacement Reactions. *The ions in two compounds exchange parts.*

Single Displacement Reactions. *One substance displaces a part of another substance.*

Oxidation Reduction Reactions. *One substance loses electrons (oxidation) while another substance simultaneously gains electrons (reduction).*

Acid-Base Reactions. *Hydrogen ions from acids combine with hydroxide ions from bases to form water.*

Part A — Oxidation Reduction Reaction: $Cu(s) \longrightarrow Cu^{2+}(aq)$

Part A is an oxidation-reduction reaction in which the oxidation of metallic copper, Cu(s) by the NO_3^- ion from HNO_3 gives a blue, aqueous solution of Cu^{2+} ions. Simultaneous reduction of NO_3^- ions gives a brown gas, NO_2 (Eq. 1, la and lb). (NOTE: "a" equations are total ionic and "b" equations are net ionic.)

$$Cu(s) + 4HNO_3(aq) \longrightarrow Cu(NO_3)_2(aq) + 2NO_2(g) + 2H_2O(l) \quad \text{(Eq. 1)}$$

$$Cu(s) + 4[H^+(aq) + NO_3^-(aq)] \longrightarrow [Cu^{2+}(aq) + 2NO_3^-(aq)] + 2NO_2(g) + 2H_2O(l) \quad \text{(Eq. 1a)}$$

$$Cu(s) + 4H^+(aq) + 2NO_3^-(aq) \longrightarrow Cu^{2+}(aq) + 2NO_2(g) + 2H_2O(l) \quad \text{(Eq. 1b)}$$

The representation of the formulas for ions in aqueous solution is a convenient oversimplification. Ions in aqueous solution, as well as in many solids, have water molecules attached to the ions. i.e. the ions are hydrated. The exact degree of hydration in aqueous solution is known for relatively few ions. Copper(II) ions usually exist in the solid state as $[Cu(OH_2)_4]^{2+}$ ions. H_2O is written OH_2 to indicate Cu—O bonds. Compounds such as copper(II) nitrate and copper(II) sulfate would be sources of Cu^{2+} ions. The blue color of dilute aqueous solutions of copper(II) nitrate and copper(II) sulfate is attributed to the presence of $[Cu(OH_2)_4]^{2+}$ ions. Because color is not normally associated with chloride, nitrate, or sulfate ions in aqueous solution, the fact that aqueous solutions of copper(II) chloride are green, while solutions of copper(II) nitrate and copper(II) sulfate are blue, indicates that $[Cu(OH_2)_4]^{2+}$ ions probably do not exist in solution of copper(II) chloride. Or, if $[Cu(OH_2)_4]^{2+}$ ions do exist, some other colored species must also be present in the solution to cause the color to be green rather than blue. It is generally accepted that the green color of copper(II) chloride solution is due to $[Cu(OH_2)_{4-n}(Cl)_n]^{(2-n)}$ In these species the number of chloride ions, "n," may vary from one to four depending on the concentration of chloride ions in the solution.

Part B — Metathetical Reaction $Cu^{2+}(aq) \longrightarrow Cu(OH)_2(s)$

In Part B a solution of NaOH(aq) neutralizes the acidic solution (Part A) in an acid-base or metathetical reaction (Eq. 2, 2a, 2b). After the neutralization of H^+ ions by the base, addition of more base increases the OH^- concentration.

$$NaOH(aq) + HNO_3(aq) \longrightarrow NaNO_3(aq) + H_2O(l) \quad \text{(Eq. 2)}$$

$$[Na^+(aq) + OH^-(aq)] + [H^+(aq) + NO_3^-(aq)] \longrightarrow [Na^+(aq) + NO_3^-(aq)] + H_2O(l) \quad \text{(Eq. 2a)}$$

$$OH^-(aq) + H^+(aq) \longrightarrow H_2O(l) \quad \text{(Eq. 2b)}$$

You can use red litmus to test for the point where the addition of the base is sufficient to give a basic solution. The excess OH^- ions react with the $Cu^{2+}(aq)$ to form the insoluble light blue hydroxide, $Cu(OH)_2(s)$ (Eq. 3, 3a, and 3b).

$$Cu(NO_3)_2(aq) + 2NaOH(aq \longrightarrow Cu(OH)_2(s) + 2NaNO_3(aq) \quad \text{(Eq. 3)}$$

$$[Cu^{2+}(aq) + 2NO_3^-(aq)] + 2[Na^+(aq) + OH^-(aq)] \longrightarrow Cu(OH)_2(s) + 2[Na^+(aq) + NO_3^-(aq)] \quad \text{(Eq. 3a)}$$

$$Cu^{2+}(aq) + 2OH^-(aq) \longrightarrow Cu(OH)_2(s) \quad \text{(Eq. 3b)}$$

The formation of the solid $Cu(OH)_2$ is the driving force that leads to the net change (Eq. 3b). You will observe the change taking place by the disappearance of the blue $Cu^{2+}(aq)$ ion and the appearance of the light blue precipitate, $Cu(OH)_2(s)$.

Part C — Decomposition Reaction. $Cu(OH)_2(s) \rightarrow CuO(s)$

When you heat the solution containing the light blue solid, $Cu(OH)_2$, a decomposition reaction occurs (Eq. 4). This forms the black solid, CuO, and H_2O. After filtering, drying and weighing the CuO you will calculate the theoretical yield of CuO from the initial (Part A) mass of Cu(s). Then you will calculate the percent recovery of Cu as CuO.

$$Cu(OH)_2(s) \longrightarrow CuO(s) + H_2O(l) \quad \text{(Eq. 4)}$$

Part D — Metathetical or Double Displacement Reaction. $CuO(s) \longrightarrow Cu^{2+}(aq)$

Although CuO is insoluble in water it dissolves in acidic solutions. HCl(aq) reacts with CuO in this metathetical reaction (Eq. 5). The formation of the weak electrolyte, H_2O, is the driving force that gives a net change (Eq. 5b). Recall that aqueous solutions of $CuCl_2$ are green (Part A).

$$CuO(s) + 2HCl(aq) \longrightarrow CuCl_2(aq) + H_2O(l) \quad \text{(Eq. 5)}$$

$$CuO(s) + 2[H^+(aq) + Cl^-(aq)] \longrightarrow [Cu^{2+}(aq) + 2Cl^-(aq)] + H_2O(l) \quad \text{(Eq. 5a)}$$

$$CuO(s) + 2H^+(aq) \longrightarrow Cu^{2+}(aq) + H_2O(l) \quad \text{(Eq. 5b)}$$

Part E — Acid-Base Reaction. $Cu^{2+}(aq) \longrightarrow [Cu(NH_3)_4]^{2+}(aq)$

Copper(II) chloride is a soluble compound. It reacts with a *limited amount* of the weak base, aqueous ammonia, to precipitate insoluble $Cu(OH)_2(s)$ (Eq. 6).

$$CuCl_2(aq) + 2NH_3(aq) + 2H_2O(l) \longrightarrow Cu(OH)_2(s) + 2NH_4Cl(aq) \quad \text{(Eq. 6)}$$

If excess aqueous ammonia is added, $Cu(OH)_2$ dissolves to form the soluble, deep blue copper-ammonia complex ion, $[Cu(NH_3)_4]^{2+}(aq)$ and OH^- ions (Eq 7).

$$Cu(OH)_2(s) + 4NH_3(aq) \longrightarrow [Cu(NH_3)_4]^{2+}(aq) + 2OH^-(aq) \quad \text{(Eq. 7)}$$

Part F — Displacement and Acid-base Reaction. $[Cu(NH_3)_4]^{2+}(aq) \longrightarrow Cu^{2+}(aq)$

Recall that aqueous solutions of copper sulfate contain hydrated Cu^{2+} ions $[Cu(OH_2)_4]^{2+}$ rather than Cu^{2+} ions. This part of the experiment illustrates a displacement reaction. The reaction of sulfuric acid with the complex compound prepared in part E can be represented as:

$$[Cu(NH_3)_4](OH)_2(aq) + 2H_2O + 3H_2SO_4(aq) \longrightarrow [Cu(OH_2)_4]SO_4(aq) + 2(NH_4)_2SO_4(aq) \quad \text{(Eq. 8)}$$

$$[Cu(NH_3)_4]^{2+}(aq) + 2OH^-(aq)\} + 2H_2O + 3[2H^+(aq) + SO_4^{2-}(aq)] \longrightarrow \{[Cu(OH_2)_4]^{2+}(aq) + SO_4^{2-}(aq)\} + 2[2NH_4^+(aq) + SO_4^{2-}(aq)] \quad \text{(Eq. 8a)}$$

$$[Cu(NH_3)_4]^{2+}(aq) + 2OH^-(aq) + 2H_2O + 6H^+(aq) \longrightarrow [Cu(OH_2)_4]^{2+}(aq) + 4NH_4^+(aq) \quad \text{(Eq. 8b)}$$

H_2O molecules replace NH_3 molecules in the complex ion, $[Cu(NH_3)_4]^{2+}$, as H^+ ions and NH_3 react to form NH_4^+ ions (Eqs. 8, 8a and 8b). Equation 8 also contains acid-base reactions (Eqs. 10 & 11). Note that the H^+ ions from H_2SO_4 combine with OH^- ions to give H_2O in a typical acid-base reaction (Eq. 11).

$4H^+(aq) + 4NH_3 \text{ (in } [Cu(NH_3)_4]^{2+}) \longrightarrow 4NH_4^+(aq)$ (Eq. 9)

$2H^+(aq) + 2OH^-(aq \longrightarrow 2H_2O(l)$ (Eq. 10)

Part G — Oxidation-reduction and Single Displacement Reactions. $Cu^{2+}(aq) \rightarrow Cu(s)$

An active metal, magnesium, will reduce copper(II) ions in the solution (Part F) to metallic copper. The metallic magnesium in turn is oxidized to magnesium ions, Mg^{2+}(Eqs. 11, 11a, and 11b). The Cu^{2+} and Mg^{2+} ion are hydrates in solution, but are written as unhydrated ions to emphasize that this is a single displacement reaction. This reaction is also an oxidation-reduction reaction. An excess of Mg metal is used to insure that all the copper(II) ions are converted to copper metal.

$CuSO_4(aq) + Mg(s) \longrightarrow MgSO_4(aq) + Cu(s)$ (Eq. 11)

$Cu^{2+}(aq) + SO_4^{2-}(aq) + Mg(s) \longrightarrow Mg^{2+}(aq) + SO_4^{2-}(aq) + Cu(s)$ (Eq. 11a)

$Cu^{2+}(aq) + Mg(s) \longrightarrow Mg^{2+}(aq) + Cu(s)$ (Eq. 11b)

The Mg that remains reacts with the excess H_2S0, from Part F (Eq. 12.)

$Mg(s) + H_2SO_4(aq) \longrightarrow MgSO_4(aq) + H_2(g)$ (Eq. 12)

CAUTION! YOU MUST WEAR DEPARTMENTALLY APPROVED EYE PROTECTION AT ALL TIMES YOU ARE IN THE LABORATORY!! KEEP ALL REACTION VESSELS WELL AWAY FROM YOUR FACE!!

PROCEDURE

FOR A ONE PERIOD LABORATORY EXPERIMENT, OMIT STEPS 14,17-21 OR OMIT PARTS D, E, F, AND G.

Part A— Oxidation Reduction Reaction: $Cu(s) \longrightarrow Cu^{2+}(aq)$

Step 1. Your instructor will give you a **piece of copper wire** weighing about 0.2-0.3 grams as the starting material. Do not handle the wire with your fingers. Record the identification number of your unknown on your REPORT FORM (1). (NOTE: Your instructor will tell you if you are to weigh the sample.)

Step 2. Weigh the **copper wire** to the nearest 0.001 gram. Record this value on the REPORT FORM (2). Bend the wire so that it lies flat on the bottom of a 250 mL bea-

CAUTION! HNO_3 (NITRIC ACID) IS A CORROSIVE ACID. IF YOU SPILL ANY ON YOUR SKIN OR CLOTHING, WASH IMMEDIATELY WITH WATER. IF YOU GET ANY YOUR EYES WASH YOUR EYES GENTLY WITH LOTS OF WATER AND GET YOUR INSTRUCTOR'S HELP IMMEDIATELY!! AVOID BREATHING THE FUMES OF THE BROWN GAS, NO_2!! DON'T HOLD YOUR HEAD OVER THE REACTION VESSEL! CARRY OUT STEPS 3-5 IN A FUME HOOD. IF YOU DO NOT HAVE A HOOD, YOUR LAB INSTRUCTOR MAY CHOOSE TO IMPROVISE AS DESCRIBED IN I.3 OF LABORATORY TECHNIQUES.

Step 3. Measure **8 mL of 6 M HNO_3** into a 10 or 25 mL graduated cylinder.

Step 4. Add the HNO_3 to the Cu(s) in the 250 mL beaker, **USING GREAT CARE!**

Step 5. Place the beaker containing Cu and HNO_3 in a 500 mL beaker containing about **100 mL of water** (Figure 2). Heat the water to a gentle boil. (NOTE: Be patient! It may require about 10-15 minutes to dissolve the copper.) Observe the blue color of the solution. When the copper has dissolved, remove the beaker from the bath, allow it to cool and **CAREFULLY** add **35 mL of H_2O** to the copper solution. Save the solution for Part B. Show this solution to your instructor.

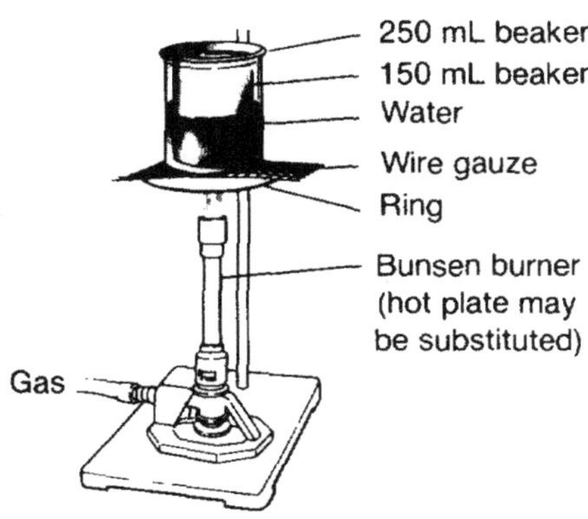

Figure 2. Water Bath.

Part B — Acid-Base Reaction: $Cu^{2+}(aq) \longrightarrow Cu(OH)_2(s)$

> **CAUTION! NaOH (SODIUM HYDROXIDE) IS A CORROSIVE BASE. HANDLE WITH CARE. IF YOU SPILL ANY ON YOUR SKIN OR CLOTHING, WASH IMMEDIATELY WITH WATER. IF YOU GET ANY IN YOUR EYES, WASH YOUR EYES GENTLY WITH LOTS OF WATER AND GET YOUR INSTRUCTOR'S HELP IMMEDIATELY!!**

Step 6. Pour **12 mL of 4 *M* NaOH** into a small graduated cylinder.

Step 7. SLOWLY add **4 *M* NaOH** with an eye dropper to the blue $Cu(NO_3)_2$ solution from Part A while stirring gently. Continue to add the NaOH solution until a precipitate remains. (NOTE: $Cu(OH)_2$ will precipitate where the drop of NaOH causes the concentration of hydroxide to be high. The precipitate will dissolve again if acid is still present.) Allow the light blue precipitate, $Cu(OH)_2$, to settle. Then allow **1 drop of 4 *M* NaOH** to flow down the side of the beaker into the clear liquid. If no additional precipitate forms, the reaction is complete. If necessary add more 4 *M* NaOH a few drops at a time while stirring until precipitation is complete.

Step 8. When all of the Cu^{2+} ions have reacted completely with OH^- ions, the excess **OH^-** ions will cause the solution to be basic. Test for the basicity by putting a drop of the solution from the stirring rod on red litmus paper.

Step 9. Show the light blue precipitate to your instructor and save it for Part C.

Part C — Decomposition Reaction. $Cu(OH)_2(s) \longrightarrow CuO(s)$

Step 10. To the beaker containing the light blue solid, $Cu(OH)_2$ from Part B, add enough **distilled water** to give a volume of approximately 100 mL.

CAUTION! RECALL THAT THIS IS AN ALKALINE SOLUTION. WHEN ALKALINE SOLUTIONS BOIL THEY TEND TO SPATTER OR BUMP! ALWAYS KEEP YOUR HANDS AND FACE AWAY FROM THE REACTION VESSEL!

Step 11. Boil the mixture *gently* for five minutes while stirring constantly to prevent spattering. (NOTE: When the reaction is complete, the solution will be colorless and the black precipitate of CuO will settle to the bottom of the beaker.)

Step 12. Add **10 drops of phenolphthalein (PP)** to the solution. (NOTE: PP is red in basic solution and colorless in neutral or in acidic solutions.) (NOTE: The solution will be made less basic by the addition of acetic acid, CH_3COOH, so that the precipitate will be easier to filter.) Strong bases tend to swell the fibers of the filter paper making the pores smaller.

Step 13. Now add **6 *M* CH_3COOH** *one drop at a time with constant stirring* until the red color of the solution *just disappears.* (NOTE: Let the solid settle between drops so you can see the color of the solution. If you add too much acid, the CuO will dissolve and you must go back to step 7.)

Step 14. To determine the mass of the CuO, weigh a piece of filter paper to the nearest 0.001 gram. Record this mass on the REPORT FORM (14). Prepare the piece of filter paper as shown in the Laboratory Techniques section 1 of this manual.

Step 15. Place the folded filter on a filter funnel which has been mounted with a clamp or iron ring on a ring stand (Figure 3). Pour some **distilled water** through the filter paper so that the paper seals to the top edge of the funnel. Discard this filtrate.

Step 16. Slowly pour the mixture containing the CuO onto the filter. Wash all the black CuO from the beaker onto the filter with water. Discard this filtrate. (NOTE: If the filtrate is blue in color, you have dissolved some CuO.) Save the black CuO for *Part D.*

CAUTION! BOTH ETHYL ALCOHOL AND ACETONE ARE HIGHLY FLAMMABLE. DO NOT USE AROUND FLAMES!

(If your instructor decides that Steps 17-21 are optional, go to Step 22.)

Step 17. Partially dry the filter paper and Cu by dropping **10 mL of ethyl alcohol** (FLAMMABLE) around the top of the filter paper and allow it to drain. Repeat with **10 mL of acetone** (FLAMMABLE).

Step 18. Carefully remove the filter paper and Cu. Spread the filter paper on three thicknesses of filter paper. Then dry it under a drying lamp or in an oven for a few minutes.

Step 19. Weigh the filter paper and CuO to the nearest 0.001 g. Record this mass on the REPORT FORM (19). (NOTE: The procedure for Part D will be carried out directly on the filter paper containing the black CuO from Part C.)

Step 20. Calculate the weight of the experimental yield of CuO and the percent yield of CuO based on the original mass of the copper wire, record on the REPORT FORM (20).

Step 21. Show the black CuO to your instructor and save it for Part D.

FOR A TWO PERIOD LABORATORY, STOP HERE.

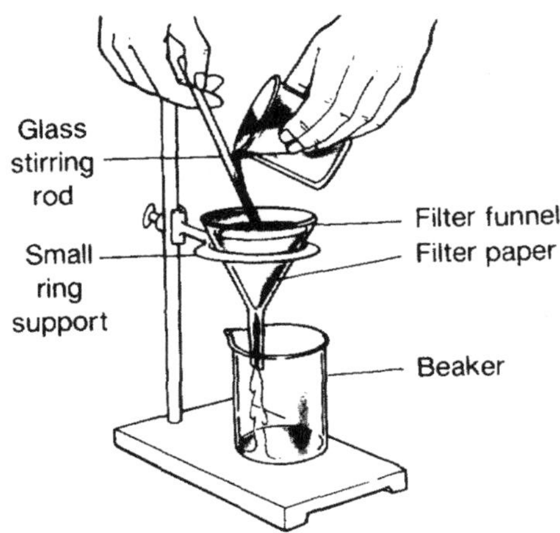

Figure 3 Filtering CuO.

Part D — Metathetical or Double Displacement Reaction.

$$CuO(s) \longrightarrow Cu^{2+}(aq)$$

> **CAUTION! HCl (HYDROCHLORIC ACID) IS A CORROSIVE ACID. HANDLE WITH CARE! WASH IT OFF IMMEDIATELY IF YOU GET IT ON YOU!**

Step 22. Obtain **5 mL of 6 *M* HCl.**

Step 23. Place a clean beaker under the filter apparatus to collect the filtrate. Place the filter paper with CuO (Step 19) in the filter funnel.

Step 24. Use an eye dropper to add the **6 *M* HCl** dropwise directly on the CuO on the filter paper. Collect the green solution in the clean beaker.

Step 25. Use the eye dropper to transfer the green solution from the beaker back over the CuO on the filter until all the CuO dissolves. If undissolved CuO still remains, wash it with fresh **6 *M* HCl,** 1 mL at a time, until all CuO has dissolved.

Step 26. Finally wash the adhering copper ions off the filter paper with 5 mL of **distilled water.** Collect all washings in the beaker along with green solution.

Step 27. Show this green solution of $CuCl_2$ to your instructor and save for Part E.

Part E — Acid-Base Reaction. $Cu^{2+}(aq) \longrightarrow [Cu(NH_3)_4]^{2+}(aq)$

> **CAUTION! NH_3 (AMMONIA) HAS AN INTENSE PUNGENT, SUFFOCATING ODOR. INHALATION OF VAPORS CAUSES SEVERE RESPIRATORY PROBLEMS. WEARING CONTACT LENSES DURING THIS EXPERIMENT COULD BE DANGEROUS TO YOUR EYES. IF YOU GET ANY IN YOUR EYES WASH YOUR EYES GENTLY WITH LOTS OF WATER AND GET YOUR INSTRUCTOR'S HELP IMMEDIATELY!!**

Perform Steps 28 and 29 in a well-vented hood.

Step 28. Pour **10 mL of 6 M aqueous ammonia** solution into a small graduated cylinder.

Step 29. Using an eye dropper, add the **6 *M* aqueous ammonia** *slowly with constant stirring* to the green solution of $CuCl_2$ from Part D until all the $Cu(OH)_2$ which forms initially just dissolves,

Step 30. Show your deep blue solution to your instructor and save it for Part F.

Part F —Displacement and Acid-base Reaction.

$$[Cu(NH_3)_4]^{2+}(aq) \longrightarrow Cu^{2+}(aq)$$

CAUTION! H_2SO_4 (SULFURIC ACID) IS A CORROSIVE, OXIDIZING ACID. IF YOU SPILL ANY ON YOUR SKIN OR CLOTHING, WASH IMMEDIATELY WITH WATER. IF YOU GET ANY IN YOUR EYES, WASH YOUR EYES GENTLY WITH LOTS OF WATER AND GET YOUR INSTRUCTOR'S HELP IMMEDIATELY!! NEVER ADD WATER TO AN ACID OR BASE SOLUTION. CAUTIOUSLY ADD THE ACID OR BASE TO WATER.

Step 31. Cautiously add **10 mL of 6 *M* H_2SO_4** a few drops at a time to the deep blue solution from Part E. (NOTE: A great deal of heat is generated in this reaction and the solution may become very hot. **Handle the solution very carefully!**) After all the H_2SO_4 has been added, the solution will be sky blue in color as it was in Parts B and D, because the $[Cu(OH_2)_4]^{2+}$ ion is in solution.

Step 32. Show the solution from Step 31 to your instructor and save it for Part G.

Part G — Oxidation-reduction and Simple Displacement Reactions.

$$Cu^{2+}(aq) \longrightarrow Cu(s)$$

Step 33. Add about **0.50 gram of magnesium turnings** to the blue $[Cu(OH_2)_4]^{2+}$ solution from Part F. (NOTE: Magnesium sulfate solution is colorless and thus the disappearance of the blue color from the solution shows that all the copper(II) ions have been displaced from solution. The complete dissolution of the magnesium is indicated by a uniformly copper-colored (reddish-brown) precipitate and the absence of bubbles of hydrogen being evolved.)

Step 34. When you believe that all the Cu^{2+} ions have been reduced and the magnesium has dissolved, add **5 mL of 6 *M* H_2SO_4** (AGAIN WITH GREAT CARE), stir vigorously and observe carefully for additional bubbles of hydrogen. If no hydrogen bubbles form, the reaction is complete.

Step 35. Allow the copper to settle to the bottom of the beaker and carefully pour off most of the liquid. Exercise care not to pour out any copper!

Step 36. Weigh a piece of filter paper to the nearest 0.001 g. Record this mass on the REPORT FORM (36).

Step 37. Use this piece of filter paper to set up your filter funnel as in Step 15.

Step 38. Pour the mixture through the funnel to transfer the copper onto the filter paper. Use your wash bottle to transfer any copper that remains in the beaker onto the filter paper.

Step 39. Dry the metallic copper by washing it with **10 mL of ethyl alcohol and 10 mL of acetone** (BOTH ARE FLAMMABLE) as in Part C, Steps 17 and 18.

Step 40. Weigh the dry filter paper and copper to the nearest 0.001 g. Record this value on the REPORT FORM (40). Show your metallic copper to your instructor.

Step 41. Calculate the mass of copper and the percent recovery of copper that you obtained on the REPORT FORM (41).

Name ______________________ Lab Instructor ______________________

Date ______________________ Lab Section ______________________

Prelab Questions

1. a. What is the maximum mass of HNO_3 which would be required to react with 0.350 g of copper metal as shown in Equation 1?

   b. What volume of 6.0 *M* HNO_3 would contain the mass of HNO_3 calculated in 1.a?

   c. If you used 12 mL of 6.0 *M* HNO_3 to dissolve the sample of copper, what volume of 4.0 M NaOH would be required to neutralize the **excess** HNO_3?

2. How will you convert copper(II) ions to copper in Part G? Write the equation for the change.

3. Why was magnesium added in Part G of the experiment?

4. a. What volume of 6.0 *M* HCl would be required to dissolve 0.402 g of CuO?

b. If you used 6.0 mL of 6.0 *M* HCl to dissolve the sample of CuO, what volume of 6.0 *M* ammonia will be required to neutralize the **excess** acid?

5. A student dissolved a piece of copper wire, then converted it to CuO, filtered the CuO from solution, and determined the mass of the CuO. The CuO was then dissolved, reduced to copper metal, and recovered. Calculate the percent yield for CuO and Cu from the following data:

Mass of the copper wire	0.246 g
Mass of filter paper	0.526 g
Mass of filter paper + CuO	0.829 g
Mass of filter paper	0.479 g
Mass of filter paper + Cu	0.702 g

% Yield CuO ____________

% Yield Cu ____________

REPORT FORM

A Sequence of Chemical Reactions

Name ______________________

Lab Instructor ______________________

Lab Section ______________________

Date ______________________

As you perform the experiment, obtain your instructor's approval at each step. As the instructor views the product obtained in each step of this experiment, your Lab Instructor will initial this sheet to indicate approval.

______________________ 1. Copper(II) nitrate solution (Step 5)

______________________ 2. Copper(II) hydroxide, a solid (Step 9)

______________________ 3. Copper(II) oxide, a solid (Step 21)

______________________ 4. Copper(II) chloride solution (Step 27)

______________________ 5. Soluble complex compound, $[Cu(NH_3)_4](OH)_2$ (Step 30)

______________________ 6. Copper(II) sulfate solution (Step 32)

______________________ 7. Metallic copper (Step 40)

Part A

Step No.

1. Identification Number of Unknown __________

2. Mass of copper wire __________ g

Part C. (may be optional)

19. Mass of filter paper+ CuO __________ g

14. Mass of filter paper __________ g

20. Mass of CuO (Experimental Yield) __________ g

Calculate the mass of CuO which could be produced from the Cu wire of Part A.

Theoretical Yield __________ g CuO

Calculate the percent yield of CuO produced in Part C.

$$\text{\% Yield} = \frac{\text{Experimental Yield CuO}}{\text{Theoretical Yield CuO}} \times 100$$

percent yield __________%

Part G.

40. Mass filter paper + Cu __________ g

36. Mass filter paper __________ g

41. Mass Cu __________ g

Calculate the % recovery of Cu based on the mass of Cu wire in Part A.

% Recovery __________

Name ______________________ Lab Instructor ______________________

Date ______________________ Lab Section ______________________

Post-Lab Questions

1. After you filtered the CuO from solution, the solution was clear and colorless. What does this indicate and how would this influence the percent yield? Begin by stating which data item would be in error and explain whether the percent yield would be too large, too small or not affected at all.

2. You added a 1.5 mL of **excess** of CH_3COOH in Step 13. Explain how this would affect the percent yield of copper oxide as you did in question 1.

3. How would the calculated percent yield of copper in Step 41 be affected (too large, too small, no affect) by the following observations? Explain each.

   a. You did not add enough H_2SO_4 in Step 34 and very little H_2 was formed.

b. Although the instructions in Step 33 called for “about 0.3 g of magnesium turnings”, you added 0.25 g of magnesium. Your original copper wire had a mass of 0.241 g.

c. The filter paper in Step 40 still had a strong oder of acetone after you weighed the paper and residue.

THE ALKALINE EARTHS AND THE HALOGENS—TWO FAMILIES IN THE PERIODIC TABLE

The Periodic Table arranges the elements in order of increasing atomic number in horizontal rows of such length that elements with similar properties recur periodically; that is, they fall directly beneath each other in the Table. The elements in a given vertical column are referred to as a family or group. The physical and chemical properties of the elements in a given family change gradually as one goes from one element in the column to the next. By observing the trends in properties the elements can be arranged in the order in which they appear in the Periodic Table. In this experiment we will study the properties of the elements in two families in the Periodic Table, the alkaline earths (Group 2) and the halogens (Group 7).

The alkaline earths are all moderately reactive metals and include barium, beryllium, calcium, magnesium, radium, and strontium. (Since beryllium compounds are rarely encountered and often very poisonous, and radium compounds are highly radioactive, we will not include these two elements in this experiment.) All the alkaline earths exist in their compounds and in solution as M^{2+} cations (Mg^{2+}, Ca^{2+}, etc.). If a solution containing one of these cations is mixed with one containing an anion (CO_3^{2-}, SO_4^{2-}, IO_3^-, etc.), an alkaline earth salt will precipitate if the compound containing those two ions is insoluble.

For example:

$$M^{2+}(aq) + SO_4^{2-}(aq) \rightarrow MSO_4(s) \quad \text{if } MSO_4 \text{ is insoluble} \quad (1a)$$

$$M^{2+}(aq) + 2\ IO_3^-(aq) \rightarrow M(IO_3)_2(s) \quad \text{if } M(IO_3)_2 \text{ is insoluble} \quad (1b)$$

We would expect, and indeed observe, that the solubilities of the salt of the alkaline earth cations with any one of the given anions show a smooth trend consistent with the order of the cations in the Periodic Table. That is, as we go from one end of the alkaline earth family to the other, the solubilities of, say, the sulfate salts either gradually increase or decrease. Similar trends exist for the carbonates, oxalates, and iodates formed by those cations. By determining such trends in this experiment, you will be able to confirm the order of the alkaline earths in the Periodic Table.

The elementary halogens are also relatively reactive. They include astatine, bromine, chlorine, fluorine, and iodine. We will not study astatine and fluorine in this experiment, since the former is radioactive and the latter is too reactive to be safe. Unlike the alkaline earths, the halogen atoms tend to gain electrons, forming X^- anions (Cl^-, Br^-, etc.). Because of this property, the halogens are oxidizing agents, species that tend to oxidize (remove electrons from) other species. An interesting and simple example of the sort of reaction that may occur arises when a solution containing a halogen (Cl_2, Br_2, I_2) is mixed with a solution containing a halide ion (Cl^-, Br^-, I^-). Taking X_2 to be the halogen, and Y^- to be a halide ion, the following reaction may occur, in which another halogen, Y_2, is formed:

$$X_2(aq) + 2\ Y^-(aq) \rightarrow 2\ X^-(aq) + Y_2(aq) \quad (2)$$

The reaction will occur if X_2 is a better oxidizing agent than Y_2, since then X_2 can produce Y_2 by removing electrons from the Y^- ions. If Y_2 is a better oxidizing agent than X_2, Reaction 2 will not proceed but will be spontaneous in the opposite direction.

In this experiment we will mix solutions of halogens and halide ions to determine the relative oxidizing strengths of the halogens. These strengths show a smooth variation as one goes from one halogen to the next in the Periodic Table. We will be able to tell if a reaction occurs by the colors we observe. In water, and particularly in some organic solvents, the halogens have characteristic colors. The halide ions are colorless in water solution and insoluble in organic solvents. Bromine (Br_2) in hexane, C_6H_{14}(HEX), is orange, while Cl_2 and I_2 in that solvent have quite different colors.

Say, for example, we shake a water solution of Br_2 with a little hexane, which is lighter than and insoluble in water. The Br_2 is much more soluble in HEX than in water and goes into the HEX layer, giving it an orange color. To that mixture we add a solution containing a halide ion, say Cl^- ion, and mix well. If Br_2 is a better oxidizing agent than Cl_2, it will take electrons from the chloride ions and will be converted to bromide, Br^-, ions; the reaction would be

$$Br_2(aq) + 2\,Cl^-(aq) \rightarrow 2\,Br^-(aq) + Cl_2(aq) \qquad (3)$$

If the reaction occurs, the color of the HEX layer will of necessity change, since Br_2 will be used up and Cl_2 will form. The color of the HEX layer will go from orange to that of a solution of Cl_2 in HEX. If the reaction does *not* occur, the color of the HEX layer will remain orange. By using this line of reasoning, and by working with the possible mixtures of halogens and halide ions, you should be able to arrange the halogens in order of increasing oxidizing power, which must correspond to their order in the Periodic Table.

One difficulty that you may have in this experiment involves terminology rather than actual chemistry. You must learn to distinguish the halogen *elements* from the halide *ions,* since the two kinds of species are not at all the same, even though their names are similar:

Elementary Halogens	*Halide Ions*
Bromine, Br_2	Bromide ion, Br^-
Chlorine, Cl_2	Chloride ion, Cl^-
Iodine, I_2	Iodide ion, I^-

The *halogens* are molecular substances and oxidizing agents, and all have odors. They are only slightly soluble in water and are much more soluble in HEX, where they have distinct colors. The *halide ions* exist in solution only in water, have no color or odor, and are *not* oxidizing agents. They do not dissolve in HEX.

Given the solubility properties of the alkaline earth cations, and the oxidizing power of the halogens, it is possible to develop a systematic procedure for determining the presence of any Group 2 cation and any Group 7 anion in a solution. In the last part of this experiment you will be asked to set up such a procedure and use it to establish the identity of an unknown solution containing a single alkaline earth halide.

Experimental Procedure

WEAR YOUR SAFETY GLASSES WHILE PERFORMING THIS EXPERIMENT 

I. Relative Solubilities of Some Salts of the Alkaline Earths

To each of four small test tubes add about 1 mL (approximately 12 drops) of 1 M H_2SO_4. Then add 1 mL of 0.1 M solutions of the nitrate salts of barium, calcium, magnesium, and strontium to those tubes, one solution to a tube. Stir each mixture with your glass stirring rod, rinsing the rod in a beaker of distilled water between stirs. Record your results on the solubilities of the sulfates of the alkaline earths in the Table, noting whether a precipitate forms, and any characteristics (such as color, amount, size of particles, and settling tendencies) that might distinguish it.

Rinse out the test tubes, and to each add 1 mL 1 M Na_2CO_3. Then add 1 mL of the solutions of the alkaline earth salts, one solution to a tube, as before. Record your observations on the solubility properties of the carbonates of the alkaline earth cations. Rinse out the tubes, and test for the solubilities of the oxalates of these cations, using 0.25 M $(NH_4)_2C_2O_4$ as the precipitating reagent. Finally, determine the relative solubilities of the iodates of the alkaline earths, using 1 mL 0.1 M KIO_3 as the test reagent.

II. Relative Oxidizing Powers of the Halogens

In a small test tube place a few milliliters of bromine-saturated water and add 1 mL of hexane. Stopper the test tube and shake until the bromine color is mostly in the HEX layer. (**CAUTIONS:** *Avoid breathing the halogen vapors. Don't use your finger to stopper the tube, since a halogen solution can give you a bad chemical burn.*) Repeat the experiment using chlorine water and iodine water with separate samples of HEX, noting any color changes as the bromine, chlorine, and iodine are extracted from the water layer into the HEX layer.

To each of three small test tubes add 1 mL bromine water and 1 mL HEX. Then add 1 mL 0.1 M NaCl to the first test tube, 1 mL 0.1 M NaBr to the second, and 1 mL 0.1 M NaI to the third. Stopper each tube and shake it. Note the color of the HEX phase above each solution. If the color is not that of Br_2 in HEX, a reaction indeed occurred, and Br_2 oxidized that anion, producing the halogen. In such a case, Br_2 is a stronger oxidizing agent than the halogen that was produced.

Rinse out the tubes, and this time add 1 mL chlorine water and 1 mL HEX to each tube. Then add 1 mL of the 0.1 M solutions of the sodium halide salts, one solution to a tube, as before. Stopper each tube and shake, noting the color of the HEX layer after shaking. Depending on whether the color is that of Cl_2 in HEX or not, decide whether Cl_2 is a better oxidizing agent than Br_2 or I_2. Again, rinse out the tubes, and add 1 mL iodine water and 1 mL HEX to each. Test each tube with 1 mL of a sodium halide salt solution, and determine whether I_2 is able to oxidize Cl^- or Br^- ions. Record all your observations in the Table.

III. Identi cation of an Alkaline Earth Halide

Your observations on the solubility properties of the alkaline earth cations should allow you to develop a method for determining which of those cations is present in a solution containing one Group 2 cation and no other cations. The method will involve testing samples of the solution with one or more of the reagents you used in Part I. Indicate on the Data page how you would proceed.

In a similar way you can determine which halide ion is present in a solution containing only one such anion and no others. There you will need to test a solution of an oxidizing halogen with your unknown to see how the halide ion is affected. From the behavior of the halogen-halide ion mixtures you studied in Part II you should be able to identify easily the particular halide that is present. Describe your method on the Data page, obtain an unknown solution of an alkaline earth halide, and then use your procedure to determine the cation and anion that it contains.

IV. Microscale Procedure for Determining Solubilities of Alkaline Earth Salts (Optional)

Your instructor may have you carry out Part I of this experiment by a microscale approach. This method uses much smaller amounts of reagents. Plastic well plates are employed as containers, and reagents are measured out with small Beral pipettes.

Using Beral pipettes, add four drops 0.1 M $Ba(NO_3)_2$, barium nitrate, to wells A1-A4, four drops to each well. Similarly, add four drops 0.1 M $Ca(NO_3)_2$, calcium nitrate, to wells B1-B4; four drops of 0.1 M $Mg(NO_3)_2$, magnesium nitrate, to wells C1-C4, and four drops 0.1 M $Sr(NO_3)_2$, strontium nitrate, to wells D1-D4.

Then, with another Beral pipette, add four drops 1 M H_2SO_4, sulfuric acid, to wells A1-D1. In the Table, record your results on the solubilities of the sulfates of the alkaline earths. Note whether a precipitate formed, and any characteristics, such as amount, size of particles, and cloudiness, which might distinguish it.

With a different Beral pipette, add four drops of 1 M Na_2CO_3, sodium carbonate, to wells A2-D2. Record your observations on the solubilities of the carbonates of the alkaline earths. Then carry out the same sort of tests with 0.25 M $(NH_4)_2C_2O_4$, ammonium oxalate, in wells A3-D3, and finally with 0.1 M KIO_3, potassium iodate, in wells A4-D4. Note all of your observations in the Table.

SAMPLE DISPOSAL. Dispose of the reaction products from this experiment as directed by your instructor.

Experiment *Name* ______________________ *Section* __________

Data and Observations: The Alkaline Earths and the Halogens

I. Solubilities of Salts of the Alkaline Earths

	1 M H_2SO_4	1 M Na_2CO_3	0.25 M $(NH_4)_2C_2O_4$	0.1 M KIO_3
$Ba(NO_3)_2$				
$Ca(NO_3)_2$				
$Mg(NO_3)_2$				
$Sr(NO_3)_2$				

Key: P = precipitate forms; S = no precipitate

Note any distinguishing characteristics of precipitate, such as amount and degree of cloudiness.

Consider the relative solubilities of the Group 2 cations in the various precipitating reagents. On the basis of the trends you observed, list the four alkaline earths in the order in which they should appear in the Periodic Table. *Start with the one which forms the most soluble oxalate.*

most soluble __________ __________ __________ __________ least soluble

Why did you arrange the elements as you did? Is the order consistent with the properties of the cations in all of the participating reagents?

II. Relative Oxidizing Powers of the Halogens

a. Color of the halogen in solution:

	Br_2	*Cl_2*	*I_2*
Water	__________	__________	__________
HEX	__________	__________	__________

(continued on following page)

(continued)

b. Reactions between halogens and halides:

	Br^-	Cl^-	I^-
Br_2			
Cl_2			
I_2			

State initial and final colors of HEX layer. R = reaction occurs; NR = no reaction occurs.

Rank the halogens in order of their increasing oxidizing power.

weakest ____________ ____________ ____________ strongest

Is this their order in the Periodic Table?

III. Identi cation of an Alkaline Earth Halide

Procedure for identifying the Group 2 cation:

Procedure for identifying the Group 7 anion:

Observations on unknown alkaline earth halide solution:

Cation present ____________

Anion present ____________

Unknown no. ____________

Experiment 10 *Name* ______________________ *Section* __________

Advance Study Assignment: The Alkaline Earths and the Halogens

1. All of the common noble gases are monatomic and low-boiling. Their boiling points in °C are: Ne, − 245; Ar, − 186; Kr, − 152; Xe, − 107. Using the Periodic Table, predict as best you can the molecular formula and boiling point of radon, Rn, the only radioactive element in this family.

__________ __________ °C

2. Substances *A, B,* and *C* can all act as oxidizing agents. In solution, *A* is green, *B* is yellow, and *C* is red. In the reactions in which they participate, they are reduced to A^-, B^-, and C^- ions, all of which are colorless. When a solution of *A* is mixed with one containing C^- ions, the color changes from green to red.

Which species is oxidized? __________

Which is reduced? __________

When a solution of *A* is mixed with one containing B^- ions, the color remains green.

Is *A* a better oxidizing agent than *C*? __________

Is *A* a better oxidizing agent than *B*? __________

Arrange *A, B,* and *C* in order of increasing strengths as oxidizing agents.

3. You are given an unknown, colorless, solution that may contain only one salt from the following set: NaA, NaB, NaC. In solution each salt dissociates completely into the Na^+ ion and the anion A^-, B^-, or C^-, whose properties are given in Problem 2. The Na^+ ion is effectively inert. Given the availability of solutions of *A, B,* and *C,* develop a simple procedure for identifying the salt that is present in your unknown. Use the other side of this page.

EXPERIMENT

Moleclar Models: Lewis Dot Formulas, VSEPR Therory, and Valence Bond Theory

OBJECTIVE To construct models of compounds and to use Lewis Dot formulas and the Valence Shell Electron Pair Repulsion (VSEPR) Theory to predict shapes and polarity of small molecules and polyatomic ions.

CONCEPT TO BE TESTED Molecular models are useful in predicting and explaining the properties of substances. These may take the form of two dimensional Lewis dot diagrams or three dimensional ball and stick models.

Text References: (1) Whitten, K. W., Davis, R. E., and Peck, L. *General Chemistry,* 5th ed., Saunders College Publishing, Philadelphia, 1996, Chapter 7 and Chapter 8. (2) Safety pp 1-7

INTRODUCTION

Chemists find macro-sized molecular models for particles that are too small to see with the human eye useful for visualizing the physical arrangements of atoms in molecules and polyatomic ions. These three dimensional models aid in understanding properties, such as the polarity of some molecules, and the reactivity and interaction of atoms in molecules. Molecular models are ball and stick sets in which each color represents a different element. (Candy gum drops or styrofoam balls and toothpicks may also be used instead.)

A basic concept of the atomic theory is that the chemical and physical properties of a substance are determined by the distribution of outer shell (highest n value) electrons in its atoms and by the spatial arrangement of these atoms in the structure. Lewis Dot formulas are two dimensional representations that use the arrangement of outer shell electrons to give basic information on the three dimensional shapes of molecules and polyatomic ions.

Experimentally, techniques such as x-ray or neutron detraction in crystals; infra-red, Raman and microwave spectroscopy; and dipole moment measurement furnish information on the relative positions or geometric arrangement of atoms in molecules or in polyatomic ions, Experimental measurements agree very closely with models for simple molecules and ions.

The following rules and procedures are given as a guide in drawing Lewis Electron Dot Formulas.

A. LEWIS ELECTRON DOT FORMULA

1) *Arrangement of Molecular Skeleton Structure*

Rule 1. For small molecules and polyatomic ions, place the element with the lowest electronegativity in the center and arrange the more electronegative atoms around it. Hydrogen is never the central atom.

Rule 2. For oxyacids, the hydrogen atoms are usually bonded to oxygen atoms which are bonded to the less electronegative central atom.

HNO_3 [H O N (O)(O)] H_2SO_4 [H O S (O)(O) O H]

*2.) Arrangement of Electron Dots**

Step 1. Determine the number of electrons that will be needed (N) to satisfy each atom. Usually all atoms need 8 electrons each except hydrogen, which needs 2 electrons.

CS_2 N = 8 (for the C)+2 (8) (for each S) = $24e^-$

CO_3^{2-} N = 8 (for the C)+ 3(8) (for each O) = 32 e^-

Step 2. Determine the number of valence electrons available (A) from each atom. For polyatomic ions, *subtract* one electron for each *positive* charge and add one electron for each negative charge.

CS_2 A = 4 (for C)+ 2(6) (for each S) = 16 e^-

CO_3^{2-} A = 4 (for C) + 3(6) (for each O) + 2 (for –2 charge) = 24 e^-

Step 3. Calculate the number of electrons shared (S) in the molecule, S = N – A

CS_2 S = 24 – 16 = $8e^-$

CO_3^{2-} S = 32 – 24 = $8e^-$

Step 4. Place the S electrons in pairs between the central atom and each bonded atom. If all the shared electrons (Step 3) have not been used, insert pairs to make double bonds. Do not exceed the number of covalent bonds that the *outer* atom can form. (H and Gp VII=l, Gp VI=2, Gp V=3, Gp IV=4)

S :: C :: S $[O : \overset{O}{\underset{..}{C}} :: O]^{2-}$

Step 5. Calculate the number of the available electrons which are not shared *(NS)* in the molecule *(NS)* = A – S.

CS_2 *(NS)* = 16 – 8 = $8e^-$

CO_3^{2-} *(NS)* = 24 – 8 = 16 e^-

Step 6. Use the nonshared electrons (Step 5) in pairs to complete the number of electrons each atom *needs.*

:S̤ :: C :: S̤: $[:\ddot{O} : \overset{:\ddot{O}:}{C} :: \ddot{O}]^{2-}$

* There are compounds that can not be represented by these rules for Lewis Dot Formulas. The central atom may have less than 8 electrons (**BF_3**) or more than 8 electrons (**PCl_5, SF_6, XeF_4**, etc). For most of these compounds, the central atom and each outer atom are bonded by single bonds consisting of one electron from the central atom and one electron from the outer atom. If there are any extra electrons on the central atom, they are grouped as unshared pairs on the central atom.

Exercise: Circle each pair of electrons that is shared between two atoms below.

B. Electronic Geometry

1. *VSEPR Theory.*

The VSEPR theory states that regions of high electron density will arrange themselves as far apart as possible around the central atom. One region of high electron density is counted for each single, double, or triple bond, or for each unshared pair of electrons (lone pair) on the central atom. In the examples shown above, CS_2 has two regions, CO_3^{2-} has three regions, PCl_5 has five regions, SF_6 and XeF_4 have six regions. The following electronic geometries are expected for these numbers of regions of high electron density.

regions	2	3	4	5	6
geometry	Linear	Trigonal planar	Tetrahedral	Trigonal bipyramidal	Octahedral

2. *The Valence Bond Theory.*

The Valence Bond Theory proposes that the higher energy atomic orbitals on the central atom hybridize (mix) when atoms approach for bonding. Electrons in orbitals on the central atom are "promoted" to higher orbitals which were not used in the ground state. These orbitals can accept electrons from other atoms. The atomic orbitals that are hybridized give new shapes that are different from the original atomic orbitals. When atoms bond through the new hybridized orbitals, the molecule will have a characteristic shape that depends on the atomic orbitals used in hybridization.

In methane, CH_4, carbon is the "central atom" and hydrogen is the "other atoms."

Electron Orbitals For Carbon

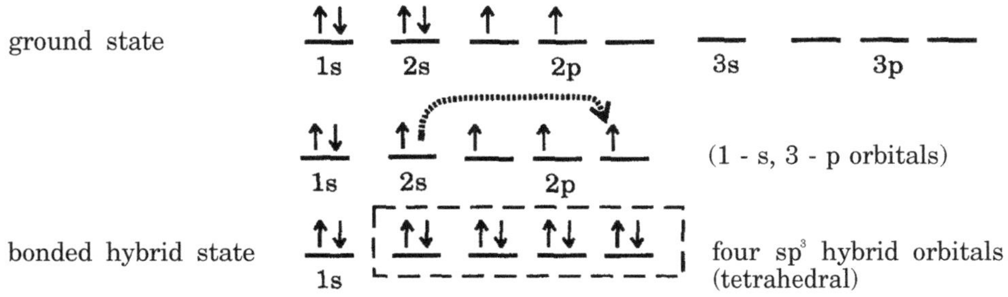

ground state: ↑↓ (1s) ↑↓ (2s) ↑ ↑ __ (2p) __ (3s) __ __ __ (3p)

↑↓ (1s) ↑ (2s) ↑ ↑ ↑ (2p) (1 - s, 3 - p orbitals)

bonded hybrid state: ↑↓ (1s) [↑↓ ↑↓ ↑↓ ↑↓] four sp^3 hybrid orbitals (tetrahedral)

The shapes of common kinds of hybrid orbitals follow:

sp	linear	dsp^2	square planar
sp^2	trigonal planar	sp^3d or dsp^3	trigonal bipyramidal
sp^3*	tetrahedral	sp^3d^2 or d^2sp^3	octahedral

* This hybridization is not used for elements in Gp V and Gp VI except in period 2. For these elements in higher periods, only atomic "p" orbitals are used in bonding. These are at right angles to each other. This still accounts for the molecular shapes of trigonal pyramidal Gp V and bent (angular) Gp IV molecules.

C. Molecular Geometry (shape)

Attach the other atoms to the regions of electron density so that these other atoms are as far apart as possible. The relative positions of the central atom and the other atoms can be described as the molecular geometry. Some examples follow.

Electronic geometry	Compound	Molecular geometry
Linear	$BeCl_2$	linear (symmetrical)

M

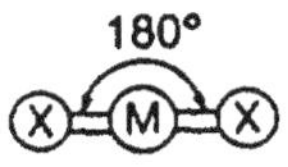

180°

X M X

Electronic geometry	Compound	Molecular geometry
Trigonal planar	SO_2	bent (unsymmetrical)
	SO_3	trigonal planar (symmetrical)
Tetrahedral	H_2O	bent (unsymmetrical)
	NH_3	trigonal pyramidal (unsymmetrical)
	CH_4	tetrahedral (symmetrical)
Trigonal bipyramidal	XeF_2	linear (symmetrical)
	ClF_3	t-shaped (unsymmetrical)

Electronic geometry	**Compound**	**Molecular geometry**
	SCl_4	seesaw (unsymmetrical) 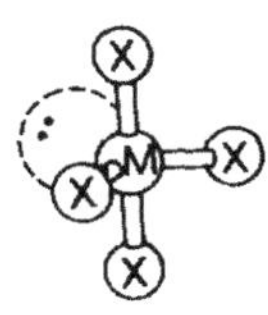
	PCl_5	trigonal bipyramidal (symmetrical) 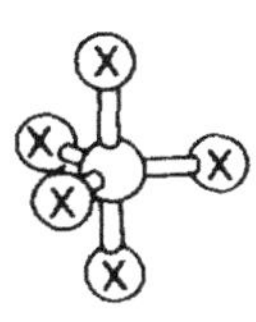
Octahedral 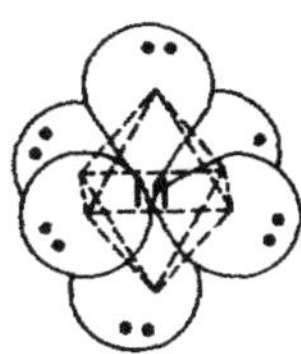	**XeF_4**	square planar (symmetrical) 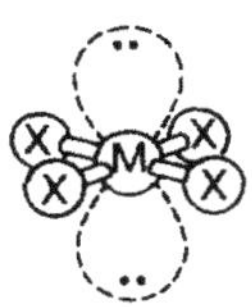
	IF_5	square pyramidal (unsymmetrical) 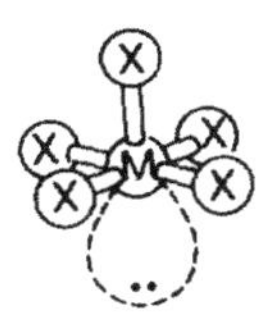
		octahedral (symmetrical) 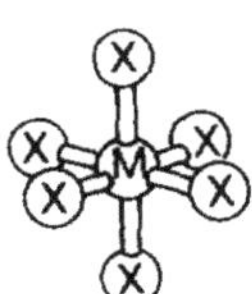

D. MOLECULAR POLARITY (DIPOLE MOMENT)

If its molecular geometry is *completely* symmetrical, a molecule is nonpolar. If the molecular geometry is unsymmetrical, the molecule will be polar because of lone pairs of electrons on the central atom. Polar bonds (due to differences in the electronegativities) may re-enforce or oppose the effect of the lone pairs of electrons.

PROCEDURE

In this experiment you will predict the polarity of a series of molecules and polyatomic ions by the following process:

Lewis Dot Formula → Electronic Geometry → Stick model → Molecular Geometry → Stick model → Symmetry → Polarity

Step 1. Calculate the number of electrons needed (N), available (A), shared (S), and not shared *(NS)* and record on REPORT FORM (1).

Step 2. Draw the Lewis Dot Formula for the molecule or polyatomic ion on the REPORT FORM (2).

Step 3. Count the number of regions of high electron density. Sketch (3a) and describe the electronic geometry on the REPORT FORM (3b).

Step 4. (Optional) Draw the ground state electronic configuration of the central atom for the electrons beyond the noble gas core on the REPORT FORM (4a). Predict the atomic obritals that hybridize to account for the electronic geometry in Step 3 (4b).

Step 5. Assemble a model of the regions of high electron density using one ball for the central atom and sticks for the regions of high electron density. (NOTE: Choose balls that have holes drilled for the correct electronic geometry.)

Step 6. Add a ball to the sticks for each outer atom.

Step 7. Based upon the relative positions of the central atom and the outer atoms, sketch (7a) and describe the molecular geometry (7b) on the REPORT FORM.

Step 8. Describe the symmetry (8a) and polarity (8b) of the molecule on the REPORT FORM.

Step 9. Repeat Steps 1-8 for each compound. (NOTE: Those compounds or ions designated by an asterisk (*) do not obey the octet rule.)

Name ______________________ Lab Instructor ______________________

Date ______________________ Lab Section ______________________

Prelab Questions

1. Write the ground state electronic configurations for the following atoms or ions. Arrange the electrons in increasing major energy levels. Diagram the electronic configuration for electrons beyond the noble gas core for each particle.

As	$1s^2 2s^2 2p^6 3s^2 3p^6 3d^{10} 4s^2 4p^3$	[Ar] ↓↑ ↓↑ ↓↑ ↓↑ ↓↑ (3d) ↓↑ (4s) ↓ ↓ ↓ (4p)
Mg		
Mg^{2+}		
Cl		
Cl^-		
Fe		
Fe^{2+}		
Fe^{3+}		

2. Write the dot formula for the following atoms or ions.

Al	N	Ba	Cl
O^{2-} ion	P^{3-} ion	K^+ ion	Si

3. What is the electronic geometry about a central atom which has
(a) three regions of electron density

(b) five regions of electron density

4. What is the molecular geometry about a central atom which has the number of electron density regions and the number of attached atoms indicated below?

	no. of electron density regions	no. attached atom	molecular geometry
example:	3	2	*bent*
a.	5	4	
b.	4	3	
c.	6	5	
d.	3	3	
e.	6	4	

REPORT FORM

Molecular Models

Name ____________________

Lab Instructor ____________________

Lab Section ______ Date ______

Formula	Dot Requirement	Dot Formula	Electronic Geometry	Molecular Geometry	(Circle one)
NCl_3	(1) N = 8 + 3(8) = 32 A = 5 + 3(7) = 26 S = 6 Not shared = 20	(2) : Cl : : Cl : N : Cl :	(3a) [N with three lone-pair-bearing Cl and one lone pair] (3b) tetrahedral	(7a) N bonded to Cl, Cl, Cl (7b) Trigonal pyramidal	(8a) Symmetrical Y (N) (8b) Polar (Y) N
			(4a) ↑↓ ↑↓ ↑ ↑ ↑ — 1s 2s 2p		(4b) hybridization sp^3
HCN	(1) N = A = S = Not shared =	(2)	(3a) (3b)	(7a) (7b)	(8a) Symmetrical Y N (8b) Polar Y N
			(4a)		(4b) hybridization
H_2Se	(1) N = A = S = Not shared =	(2)	(3a) (3b)	(7a) (7b)	(8a) Symmetrical Y N (8b) Polar Y N
			(4a)		(4b) hybridization

Formula	Dot Requirement	Dot Formula	Electronic Geometry	Molecular Geometry	(Circle one)
CO_2	(1) N = A = S = Not shared =	(2)	(3a) (3b)	(7a) (7b)	(8a) Symmetrical Y N (8b) Polar Y N
			(4a)		(4b) hybridization
SeO_3^{2-}	(1) N = A = S = Not shared =	(2)	(3a) (3b)	(7a) (7b)	(8a) Symmetrical Y N (8b) Polar Y N
			(4a)		(4b) hybridization
NO_3^-	(1) N = A = S = Not shared =	(2)	(3a) (3b)	(7a) (7b)	(8a) Symmetrical Y N (8b) Polar Y N
			(4a)		(4b) hybridization

REPORT FORM

Molecular Models

Name ______________________

Lab Instructor ______________________

Lab Section ________ Date ____________

Formula	Dot Requirement	Dot Formula	Electronic Geometry	Molecular Geometry	(Circle one)
$S_2O_3^{2-}$	(1) N = A = S = Not shared =	(2)	(3a) (3b)	(7a) (7b)	(8a) Symmetrical Y N (8b) Polar Y N
			(4a)		(4b) hybridization
$POCl_3$	(1) N = A = S = Not shared =	(2)	(3a) (3b)	(7a) (7b)	(8a) Symmetrical Y N (8b) Polar Y N
			(4a)		(4b) hybridization
$CH_2Cl_2^-$	(1) N = A = S = Not shared =	(2)	(3a) (3b)	(7a) (7b)	(8a) Symmetrical Y N (8b) Polar Y N
			(4a)		(4b) hybridization

Formula	Dot Requirement	Dot Formula	Electronic Geometry	Molecular Geometry	(Circle one)
SCl_2	(1) N = A = S = Not shared =	(2)	(3a) (3b)	(7a) (7b)	(8a) Symmetrical Y N (8b) Polar Y N
			(4a)		(4b) hybridization
* ICl_4^-	(1) N = A = S = Not shared =	(2)	(3a) (3b)	(7a) (7b)	(8a) Symmetrical Y N (8b) Polar Y N
			(4a)		(4b) hybridization
* $AlCl_6^{3-}$	(1) N = A = S = Not shared =	(2)	(3a) (3b)	(7a) (7b)	(8a) Symmetrical Y N (8b) Polar Y N
			(4a)		(4b) hybridization

REPORT FORM

Molecular Models

Name____________________

Lab Instructor____________________

Lab Section________ Date__________

Formula	Dot Requirement	Dot Formula	Electronic Geometry	Molecular Geometry	(Circle one)
H_3O^+	(1) N = A = S =	(2)	(3a) (3b)	(7a) (7b)	(8a) Symmetrical Y N (8b) Polar Y N
	Not shared =		(4a)		(4b) hybridization
ClO_3^-	(1) N = A = S =	(2)	(3a) (3b)	(7a) (7b)	(8a) Symmetrical Y N (8b) Polar Y N
	Not shared =		(4a)		(4b) hybridization
PCl_4^+	(1) N = A = S =	(2)	(3a) (3b)	(7a) (7b)	(8a) Symmetrical Y N (8b) Polar Y N
	Not shared =		(4a)		(4b) hybridization

Formula	Dot Requirement	Dot Formula	Electronic Geometry	Molecular Geometry	(Circle one)
SiF_4	(1) N = A = S = Not shared =	(2)	(3a) (3b)	(7a) (7b)	(8a) Symmetrical Y N (8b) Polar Y N
			(4a)		(4b) hybridization
NO_2^-	(1) N = A = S = Not shared =	(2)	(3a) (3b)	(7a) (7b)	(8a) Symmetrical Y N (8b) Polar Y N
			(4a)		(4b) hybridization
* BrF_3	(1) N = A = S = Not shared =	(2)	(3a) (3b)	(7a) (7b)	(8a) Symmetrical Y N (8b) Polar Y N
			(4a)		(4b) hybridization

EXPERIMENT
Paper Chromatography: Qualitative Analysis of Metal Cations

Objective

To learn the principles of paper chromatography and to use the technique to analyze a mixture of metal cations.

Discussion

The usual first step in the chemical analysis of an unknown material is the separation of the different compounds that are present in the unknown. Once separated, identification of the compounds is generally much easier to accomplish. *Chromatography* separates the different compounds in a mixture by making them all start to move at the same time in the same direction by putting them in a mobile phase which is made to flow through a stationary phase. Because each compound moves at a different speed, the compounds become separated from one another and can be isolated for species identification.

Mobile phase and stationary phase

In this experiment, the sample is made to move by dissolving it into a flowing solvent, so that the sample molecules are carried along in the direction of the flow. The solvent carries the sample through a piece of filter paper, drawn by capillary action. Different compounds in the sample are attracted with different binding strengths to the paper fibers. The flowing solvent is called the *mobile phase* and the filter paper is called the *stationary phase.* The more strongly a compound binds to the stationary phase, the more slowly it is carried along by the mobile phase. After a time, the different kinds of compounds are found at different locations on the filter paper.

When the components are separated, the paper strip is removed from the solvent reservoir, stopping the solvent motion in the paper. The final distance that an unknown compound has moved along the paper is compared with the movement of known standard compounds to help identify the unknowns. This comparison is made by means of the *retention factor,* described below.

This method of separation is easy to use for homogeneous mixtures and is well suited to separating and purifying small quantities of chemicals that can be dissolved into the same solvent.

Experimental Technique

Metal ions are dissolved in a suitable solvent. A drop of the liquid sample is placed on a spot near one end of a strip of filter paper and the solvent is evaporated, leaving the metal ions adsorbed on the paper fibers. The end of the paper strip with the sample is then immersed in another solvent, the *mobile phase.* The mobile phase solvent is drawn upward through the paper fibers by capillary action. When the mobile phase solvent reaches the sample, soluble compounds in the sample are dissolved and carried along with the mobile phase as it moves through the paper. The leading edge of the mobile phase is called the *solvent front.*

In Figure 1, the behavior of three different compounds, **A, B,** and **C** is illustrated as they are separated by paper chromatography.

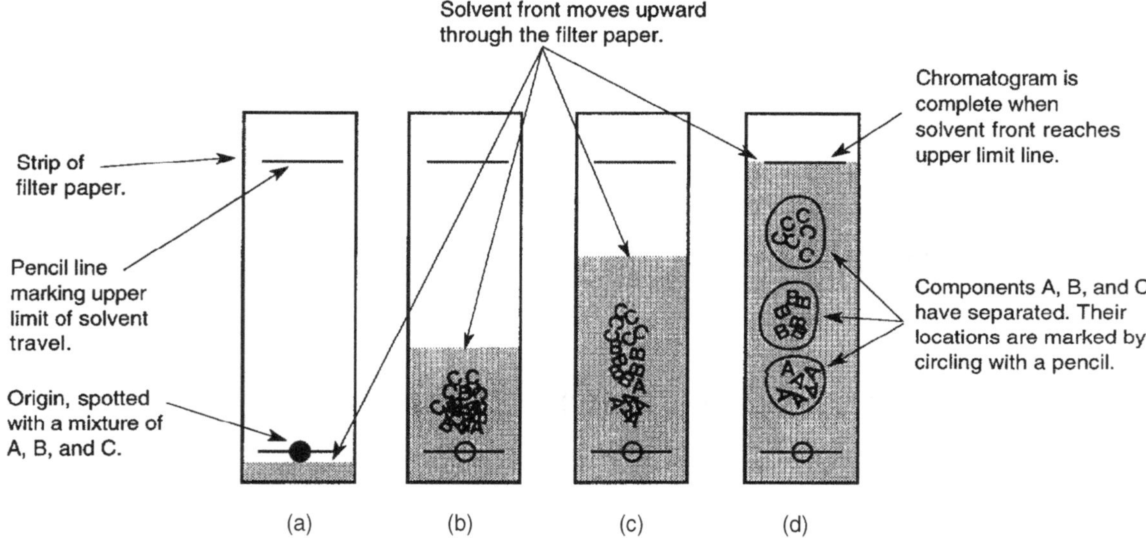

Figure 1: Illustration of the separation of a 3-component mixture of **A, B,** and **C** by paper chromatography. The shaded area represents the solvent as it moves upward through the paper strip.

(a) The solvent front has not yet reached the origin, where a mixture of **A, B,** and **C** are spotted.

(b) The solvent front passing through the origin carries with it molecules of **A, B,** and **C.** The **A** molecules bind more strongly to the stationary phase than do **B,** or **C** and move upward more slowly.

(c) As the solvent continues upward, the separation of **A, B,** and **C** becomes more complete.

(d) When the solvent reaches the line marking its upper limit, **A, B,** and **C** have separated sufficiently to allow their identification by measuring their **retention factors** (see below and Figure 4).

Retention Factor

After the separation is complete, the *retention factor* is determined as follows (see Prelaboratory Exercise, Figure 3,):

1. With a pencil, mark the position of the *solvent front,* the maximum height attained by the solvent. The solvent front is the border between the portion of the paper wetted by solvent and the dry part not yet reached by solvent.

2. Mark the positions of the separated compounds on the paper strip by outlining each spot with a pencil. Then, estimate and mark the center of each outlined spot.

3. Retention factors are obtained by measuring the distances traveled by the different compounds and by the solvent. The measurements are made from the origin, to the centers of the separated spots and to the solvent front, as in Figure 3.

$$\text{retention factor} = R_f = \frac{\text{distance traveled by the compound}}{\text{distance traveled by the solvent}}$$

Each different compound will have a characteristic retention factor, which is used to identify the compound.

Example Calculation:

After stopping the solvent flow, component **A** has moved 3.1 cm, component **B** has moved 4.2 cm, component **C** has moved 4.7 cm, and the solvent upper limit line is at 5.4 cm. The $\mathbf{R_f}$ values characteristic of **A, B,** and **C** are:

$$R_f(A) = \frac{3.1\text{ cm}}{5.4\text{ cm}} = 0.57; \quad R_f(B) = \frac{4.2\text{ cm}}{5.4\text{ cm}} = 0.78; \quad R_f(C) = \frac{4.7\text{ cm}}{5.4\text{ cm}} = 0.87$$

Safety Precautions

Wear approved eye protection.

Acetone is very flammable. Keep open flames away.

Hydrochloric acid is corrosive and will damage skin and clothing. Avoid contact. If you get any on your skin, wash immediately with copious amounts of water.

The vapors of hydrochloric acid and acetone are irritating. Use them in the hood and avoid inhalation.

Procedure

On the same piece of filter paper, you will chromatography several known solutions simultaneously with an unknown. In this way, you can be certain that the experimental variables such as temperature and composition of the solvent solution are exactly the same for your known standards and the unknown. This assures that the R_f factors can be directly compared.

Prepare the materials

1. In the hood, carefully mix together 24 mL of acetone and 10 mL of dilute hydrochloric acid.

Acetone inflammable. Keep open flames away.

Liquid hydrochloric acid is corrosive. Avoid skin contact. Wash with copious amounts of water if skin contact occurs.

Hydrochloric acid vapor is irritating. Avoid inhalation. Use only in a hood.

Pour this solvent mixture into a 1000 mL beaker and cover the beaker tightly with plastic film so that solvent vapors do not escape. The beaker volume must become saturated with solvent vapor to insure uniform solvent motion through the filter paper.

2. Obtain a piece of filter paper measuring about 25 cm by 12 cm. *With a pencil,* draw two lines parallel to the long edges, as in Figure 2. One line is 1 cm from the bottom of the strip and will be the origin. The other is 9 cm from the bottom and will be the maximum extent of the solvent travel.

All markings on the filter paper must be made with pencil. Inks contain substances that will dissolve in the moving phase and be chromatographed along with your sample.

4. Starting at the left side of the bottom (origin) line, lightly mark the line with pencil at 3 cm intervals. Then draw a small 4mm circle on the origin in the center of each interval and label each interval, as shown in Figure 2, to identify the different metal cations and unknowns.

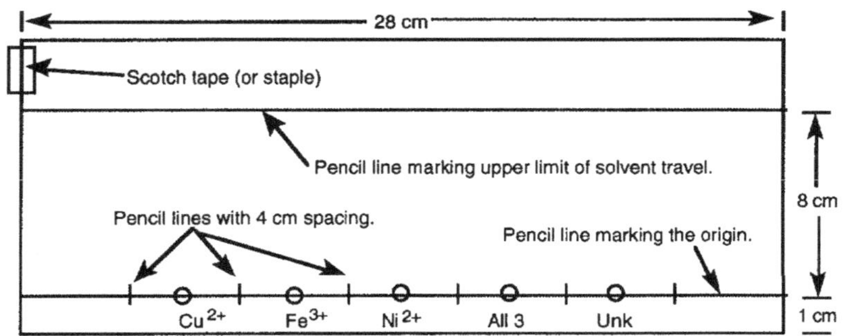

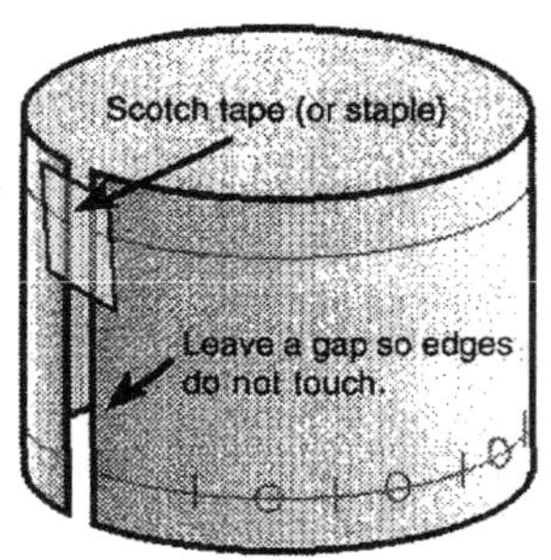

Figure 2: Preparation of chromatogram paper.

Spot the chromatogram

5. You now are ready to spot your filter paper. Follow the procedure below carefully.

a. Lay the prepared filter paper on a clean paper towel, which serves as an absorbent pad.

b. Carry your filter paper on the towel to where the metal ion samples are located. Each solution will have its own micro-capillary spotting tube (1-2 μL) already placed in it. On the 5 prepared locations, spot your filter paper with each of the following samples:

Do not mixup the spotting tubes.

1) A sample containing a soluble Fe^{3+} compound.
2) A sample containing a soluble Cu^{2+} compound.
3) A sample containing a soluble Ni^{2+} compound.
4) A sample containing a mixture of all 3 cations.
5) An unknown sample containing 1, 2, or all 3 of the cations.

c. Just lift the end of the micro-capillary spotting tube out of the solution that you are going to spot. Liquid will be held in the tube by capillary action. Touch the tip to the side of the container wall to remove the hanging drop.

Each sample is to be spotted 2 times on the same location.

d. Hold the capillary tube perpendicular to the filter paper and touch its tip *lightly* to the origin line, halfway between two division marks (see Figure 2). Allow the solution to run into the paper until the wet spot is about 5-8 mm in diameter. Allow the spot to dry and repeat the spotting procedure once more, with the same sample on the same location. Drying may be speeded with a hot-air blower or by holding the strips over a warm hotplate.

Allow each application to dry before the next is added to the same spot.

e. Repeat this procedure for each sample location on the filter paper.

Shape the filter paper

5. After the samples have been spotted and dried, shape the filter paper into a cylinder *without overlapping the edges* (as in Figure 2). Fasten only the top of the cylinder with a piece of Scotch tape or a staple. Stand the cylinder on your bench to see if it stands straight. Adjust if necessary.

6. Remove the plastic film from the beaker containing the solvent solution and carefully insert the filter paper cylinder so it stands in the solution with the origin line just a little above the solution surface, not touching the beaker wall. Immediately replace the plastic film cover on the beaker.

7. Observe the rise of solvent solution through the filter paper. When it reaches your upper limit line, remove the paper quickly and allow the solvent solution to evaporate. Do this in the hood, using an air blower to help the drying.

8. Circle any colored spots that have appeared. Write the number *1* next to these spots. Then in the hood, carefully pour a few milliliters of concentrated ammonia (sometimes labeled NH_4OH) into a 400 mL beaker and hold the chromatogram over the beaker for one full minute.

Ammonia fumes are irritating. Avoid inhalation.

Circle any new spots that become visible upon contact with the ammonia vapor. Write the number *2* next to these spots.

9. Now, while still moist with ammonia, run the paper quickly through a dimethylglyoxime solution in a shallow dish to coat the paper. Alternatively, you may use a sprayer to wet the paper with dimethylglyoxime. Ni^{2+} should turn red.

If Ni^{2+} does not turn red, hold the chromatogram over the ammonia again, while still wet with dimethylglyoxime solution.

10. Dry the paper in the hood with a blower and circle any new spots. Write the number 3 next to these spots.

11. Record on the Data Sheet the distance between the origin line and the upper limit of the solvent front. Then record for each spot observed, its distance from the origin, its color, and at which stage of development it appeared (stage 1, 2, or 3).

12. Calculate the R_f values for each sample. Be sure to show your work. For samples 4 and 5, which may contain more than one cation, you should be able to identify the metal in each spot by its color, the stage in development at which the spot appeared and its R_f value.

13. Clearly indicate on the Data Sheet which cations were in your unknown sample. Complete the Data Sheet and turn it in to your instructor. Be sure to staple your chromatogram to the Data Sheet.

Name ____ Desk _________

Date _____________ Lab Instructor/Section ______________________________

Experiment
Data Sheet

Distance from origin to upper limit of solvent travel: _____________

		Color of spot.	Which reagent (if any) made color appear?	Distance of center of spot from origin.	R_f value
Samples with single cations	Fe^{3+}				
	Cu^{2+}				
	Ni^{2+}				
Sample with all 3 cations	Fe^{3+}				
	Cu^{2+}				
	Ni^{2+}				
Ions present in Unknown No.:	Fe^{3+}				
	Cu^{2+}				
_________	Ni^{2+}				

Tape your chromatogram to this page.

Name ______________________________ Desk __________

Date ______________ Lab Instructor/Section ______________________________

Experiment
Prelaboratory Exercise

Use Figure 3 to measure some hypothetical $\mathbf{R_f}$ values for the compounds ***X, Y,*** and ***Z.*** Measure with a ruler and record the values below the figure.

Retention factor for component x = $R_f(x) = \dfrac{d_x}{D_s}$

d_x = distance from origin to the center of x spot.

D_s = distance from origin to solvent front.

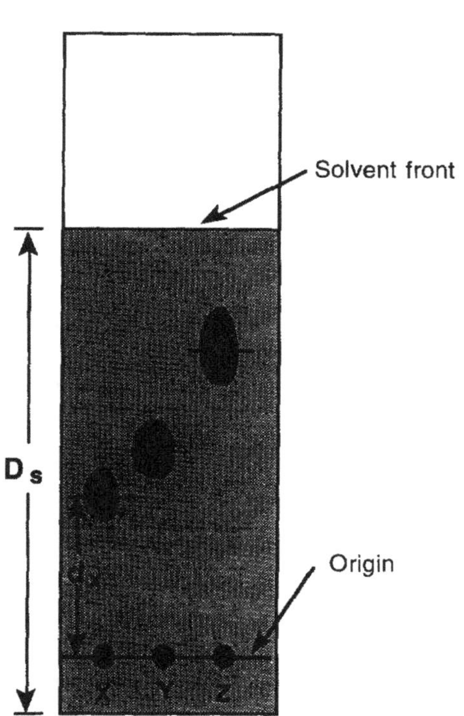

Figure 3 Measuring R_f values..

a. $\mathbf{R_f}$(X) = ______________

b. $\mathbf{R_f}$(Y) = ______________

c. $\mathbf{R_f}$(Z) = ______________

EXPERIMENT

Experimental Determination of the Ideal Gas Constant

Objective

To measure the value of the ideal gas constant for oxygen gas and compare your result with the tabulated value.

Discussion

The *Ideal Gas Law,* Equation 1, quite accurately predicts the behavior of most gases, if the gas pressure is no higher than a few atmospheres and the gas temperature is well above its condensation temperature.

$$PV = nRT \tag{1}$$

P = pressure (atm)
V = volume (L)
n = moles of gas
T = temperature (K)
R = ideal gas constant = 0.08206 L atm mol^{-1} K^{-1}

The units of *P, V,* and *R* are chosen here to be consistent and convenient for this experiment. Temperature must always be expressed in *degrees Kelvin.*

Two important assumptions are made in the derivation of the ideal-gas law:

1. Attractive and repulsive forces between gas molecules are insignificantly weak compared to their thermal energy.
2. The actual volume of the molecules themselves is negligibly small compared to the volume of their container, so that the space inside the container is essentially empty.

If these assumptions are valid for a particular gas under the experimental conditions of temperature and pressure, then Equation 1 will accurately predict the behavior of the gas. If experimentally measured pressures, volumes, and temperatures do not match Equation 1, it indicates that intermolecular forces and molecular volumes cannot be disregarded and that the gas is not behaving ideally.

Under your laboratory conditions, oxygen gas behaves as an ideal gas very closely.

In this experiment, you will measure the gas constant for oxygen gas by making a known amount of oxygen and measuring its pressure, volume, and temperature. When you insert your measured data into the ideal-gas law, you can see if you obtain the accepted value for the gas constant R, within experimental error. If you come close, then your laboratory technique has been good enough to confirm the tabulated value for the gas constant; if not, either you have made a calculation error or your lab technique is at fault.

To measure a value for R, it is necessary to have the following information:

a. the molar mass, *M,* of the gas,
b. the mass, *m,* of the measured sample,
c. values for *P, V,* and *T,* measured when the gas sample is at equilibrium.

Testing for gas ideality

These quantities are then inserted into Equation 1 and a value of R calculated. Don't expect to obtain the handbook value of

$$R = 0.08206 \text{ L-atm/mol-K}$$

exactly, even if the gas is truly ideal. There always are measuring uncertainties, and an experiment can only indicate the ideality or nonideality of a gas within experimental limits of error.

Example

Note that the temperature measurement is the least precise. This limits the calculated value of R to 3 significant figures.

Consider the following data, measured on a sample of helium gas. Measured values are given with their experimental uncertainties.

Sample data measured in an experiment on Helium:

molar mass He:	$M_{He} = 4.0026 \text{ g mol}^{-1}$ (handbook value)
measured mass of sample:	m = 0.504 ± 0.001 g
measured pressure of sample:	P = 753.6 ± 0.1 torr
measured volume of sample:	V = 3.052& 0.005 L
measured temperature of sample:	T = 21°C M 1°C = 294 ± 1 K

The ± uncertainties in the measured values can be used to find the uncertainty in the final measured value of R.

What do these measured values indicate concerning the ideality of helium gas, within the experimental limits of error? To answer this question, rewrite Equation 1 as: $R = \frac{PV}{nT}$. Substitute the relation: $n = \frac{m}{M}$ to get Equation 2:

$$R = \frac{MPV}{mT} \qquad (2)$$

Now, use Equation 2 to calculate the value of R predicted by the experimental data.

$$R_{exp} = \frac{(4.003 \text{ g/mol})(753.6 \text{ torr})(3.052 \text{ L})}{(0.504 \text{ g})(294 \text{ K})} \times \left(\frac{1 \text{ atm}}{760 \text{ torr}}\right) = 0.0817 \frac{\text{L atm}}{\text{mol K}}$$

We know that the handbook value is $R = 0.0821 \frac{\text{L atm}}{\text{mol K}}$, to 3 significant figures, so that the percent difference between R_{exp} and $R_{handbook}$ is:

$$\text{percent difference} = \frac{(0.0817 - 0.0821)}{0.0821} \times 100\% = -0.5\%$$

How significant is a difference between the experimental results and the handbook value?

How significant is this difference? Does it mean there is a small degree of nonideality for helium gas under our experimental conditions? Perhaps the discrepancy is simply due to experimental error. We cannot tell until we determine the limits of error in our calculated value for R, due to uncertainties in our measurements.

When we perform a statistical analysis of the ± uncertainties in the separate measurements of P, V, T, and mass, we find that R_{exp}, expressed with its experimental limits of error is:

$$R_{exp} = 0.0817 \pm 0.0005 \frac{\text{L atm}}{\text{mol K}}$$

Using the limits of error for the measured value of R

This means that our measured R is predicted by the experiment to have some value between:

R = 0.0817 + 0.0005 = 0.0822 and R = 0.0817 - 0.0005 = 0.0813

The handbook value, R = 0.0821 L-atm/mol-K, lies within the limits of error for this experiment. Therefore, the results of the helium experiment are that *no deviation from ideality was detected.*

Plan of the Experiment

You make oxygen gas by heating potassium chlorate ($KClO_3$) in the presence of a catalyst. The catalyst is powdered manganese dioxide (MnO_2), which speeds up the reaction without being consumed. The reaction is:

$$2\ KClO_3(s) \xrightarrow{MnO_2} 2\ KCl(s) + 3\ O_2(g)$$

You measure the mass, volume, pressure, and temperature of the O_2 and calculate a value for *R*. Then you compare your value for *R* with the handbook value, to see if they match within the experimental limits.

Mass of oxygen

The only gas given off in the reaction is oxygen. The mass of oxygen is equal to the mass lost by the solids in the reaction test tube.

Volume of oxygen

The volume of oxygen is measured by causing O_2 to displace water from a bottle, so that the displaced water flows into a beaker. The volume of displaced water is measured in a graduated cylinder. The volume of displaced water is equal to the volume of O_2 evolved.

Pressure of oxygen

The water vapor pressure depends only on the temperature of the water. It can be read from Table 1.

The pressure measurement is complicated slightly by the fact that the oxygen evolved is collected by trapping it in a bottle sealed with water. This causes the oxygen to be mixed with water vapor, which contributes to the total pressure in the flask.

The total pressure of the oxygen-water vapor mixture is found by adjusting the total pressure in the gas collection bottle so that it is the same as the external atmospheric pressure. Then, the external atmospheric pressure is measured with a barometer.

$$P(\text{external}) = \text{atmospheric pressure}; \quad P(\text{inside bottle}) = P_{O_2} + P_{\text{water vapor}}$$

When the pressures are equalized: $P(\text{external}) = P_{atm} = P_{O_2} + P_{\text{water vapor}}$

$$P_{O_2} = P_{atm} - P_{\text{water vapor}} \qquad (3)$$

Temperature of oxygen

The temperature of your collected oxygen is the laboratory room temperature.

Table 1: Vapor Pressure of Water at Selected Temperatures

Temperature (°C)	Vapor Pressure (torr)	Temperature (°C)	Vapor Pressure (torr)
15	12.8	22	19.8
16	13.6	23	21.1
17	14.5	24	22.4
18	15.5	25	23.8
19	16.5	26	25.2
20	17.5	27	26.8
21	18.7	28	28.4

Safety Precautions

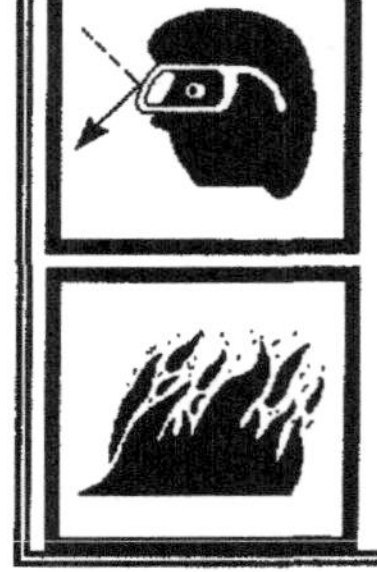

Wear approved eye protection.

Potassium chlorate ($KClO_3$) is a strong oxidizing agent that will react vigorously with many other chemicals. Do not allow it to contact other substances, especially combustible materials.

Procedure

1. Put a mixture of about 3 g $KClO_3$ and about 0.2 g MnO_2 in a large test tube.

Be sure to keep other chemicals and combustible materials away from. $KClO_3$. *Do not let* $KClO_3$ *contact the rubber stopper.*

Weigh the tube and contents to 1 mg. Record the mass on the Data Sheet.

2. Assemble the apparatus shown in Figure 1. Use a bottle or flask of ½ to 1 L capacity and a 400 mL beaker. The glass tip of an eyedropper with its constricted end can serve for glass tube *C*.

3. Fill the bottle with tap water and assemble the apparatus, except *do not* attach rubber tube *A* to the test tube yet. Add enough tap water to the beaker to cover the constricted end of the glass delivery tube by about 1 cm.

The constricted end of glass tube C must remain below the beaker water surface during these manipulations.

4. Blow into rubber tube *A* in order to force water into rubber tube *B*, filling it. Allow excess water to run into the beaker. Then raise and lower the beaker several times to move water back and forth through flexible tube *B*, in order to remove all air bubbles.

5. Raise the beaker until the water level in the bottle is a few mm below the short glass tube projecting into the bottle. Water must not enter this glass tube.

6. Close flexible tube *B* with the pinch clamp and lower the beaker to the table top. The constriction in tube *C* prevents water below the pinch clamp from draining out. Do not worry if a few drops drain out.

7. Attach the weighed test tube containing $KClO_3$ to the stopper on tube *A*..

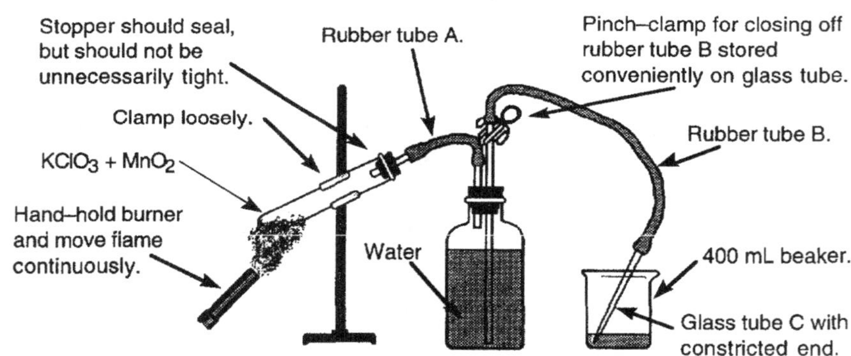

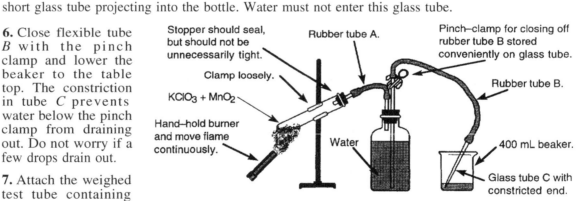

Figure 1: Apparatus for generating oxygen.

8. Check for leaky connections by opening the pinch clamp. Some water will flow into the beaker, but if there are no leaks, there will be no *continuing flow* of water out of the bottle into the beaker, even with a large difference in water level heights.

9. The pressure in the test tube and bottle must be the same as the external atmospheric pressure, so that you can measure it with a barometer. This condition is established by raising the beaker until the water levels in the beaker and bottle are the same. When the water levels are the same, close the pinch clamp on rubber tube *B,* to seal atmospheric pressure inside your apparatus, and remove constricted glass tube *C* from the beaker.

10. Empty the beaker into a sink, draining it completely, *but do not dry it.* Leaving residual water on the beaker walls will improve your volume measurement, because approximately the same amount of water will remain on the walls when you pour the water, displaced into the beaker by evolved oxygen, into a graduated cylinder to measure its volume.

11. Replace constricted glass tube C into the beaker. Remove the pinch clamp.

It is very important to remove the pinch clamp in step 11.

Do not worry if a small amount of water flows into the beaker before the flow stops. Leave this water in the beaker. This water will be measured as part of the displaced water and will not affect the accuracy of the experiment.

Obtain the instructor's approval of your apparatus before proceeding.

12. Holding the gas burner in your hand, heat the mixture in the test tube gently at first, and then more strongly, until you can see that O_2 is being evolved fast enough to maintain a moderate flow rate of water from the bottle to the beaker.

Do not heat the tube in only one spot. Move the flame about to heat the reactants uniformly.

13. Continue heating the $KClO_3$ until you have collected about 300 mL of water in the beaker.

14. Then remove the flame and allow the test tube to cool to room temperature. It will take about 10-15 minutes. As the tube cools, some water is drawn back into the bottle from the beaker, lowering the water level in the beaker.

15. After the test tube has cooled to room temperature, repeat Step 9, equalizing the internal and atmospheric pressures by adjusting the beaker height until water levels in the bottle and beaker are equal.

Be certain the constricted end of g/ass tube C remains below the beaker water surface during the cooling period and the subsequent manipulations.

16. When water levels in the beaker and bottle are equal, replace the pinch clamp on rubber tube *B.*

17. Remove the test tube and its contents and weigh them carefully. Record the mass on the Data Sheet.

The mass loss of the test tube contents is equal to the mass of oxygen evolved.

18. Pour the water collected in the beaker into a clean, dry 100 mL graduated cylinder and carefully measure the volume, You may have to fill the cylinder more than once but you do not have to dry it between fillings. Be careful not to fill it past the top mark. Drain the beaker completely. Record all the volume measurements on the Data Sheet.

The volume of water equals the volume of O_2 *generated at room temperature and atmospheric pressure.*

19. Obtain a current barometric pressure reading to determine the atmospheric pressure. Your instructor will either provide the value or explain how to get it. Record the pressure on the Data Sheet.

The barometric pressure reading is equal to the total pressure of the oxygen-water vapor mixture in the gas-collection bottle.

20. Measure room temperature by allowing a thermometer to come to thermal equilibrium with the room air. Record the temperature on the Data Sheet.

Assume that the thermometer reading is the temperature of your collected gas.

21. Determine the vapor pressure of water at your room temperature from Table 1. Record the value on the Data Sheet.

22. Calculate a value for R_{exp} from your data. Be sure to correct for the vapor pressure of water when determining the O_2 pressure. Record your value for R_{exp} on the Data Sheet.

Name ______________________________ Desk __________

Date ______________ Lab Instructor/Section ______________________________

Experiment Data Sheet

When you compare your measured value of R with the handbook value, assume the limits of error in your experiment are: $\mathbf{\Delta R = \pm 0.001 \frac{L\ atm}{mol\ K}}$

1. Mass of test tube and reactants: __________ ± __________
2. Mass of test tube and residue after heating: __________ ± __________
3. Mass of oxygen evolved: __________ ± __________
4. Volume of water displaced from bottle into beaker: __________ ± __________
   (equals O_2 volume)
   If you filled the cylinder more than once, record each filling below:
   __________ mL + __________ mL + __________ mL
5. Barometric pressure: __________ ± __________
6. Room temperature: __________ ± __________
7. Vapor pressure of water at room temperature: __________ ± __________
8. Pressure of O_2 (calculated from Equation 3) __________ ± __________

R_{exp} (calculated from above data) = __________ ± __________

Name ______________________________ Desk __________

Date ______________ Lab Instructor/Section ______________________________

Experiment
Prelaboratory Exercise

1. Oxygen gas is collected over water at 22.0°C. The pressure in the collection bottle is equilibrated with atmospheric pressure, which is measured to be 749.8 torr. What is the pressure of O_2 in the collection bottle?

____

2. Calculate the value for R_{exp} which is indicated by the following measurements on a sample of carbon dioxide gas, CO_2. Assume the limits of error are $\Delta R = \pm 0.005 \frac{\text{L atm}}{\text{mol K}}$

$$M_{CO_2} = 44.01 \text{ g/mol (handbook value)}$$
$$m = 3.7446 \text{ g}$$
$$P = 758 \text{ torr}$$
$$V = 1.898 \text{ L}$$
$$T = 0\ ^\circ\text{C}$$

$$R_{exp} = \_\_\_\_\_\_\_\_\_\_ \pm 0.005 \frac{\text{L atm}}{\text{mol K}}$$

What does this experiment indicate about the ideality of CO_2 gas under the experimental conditions?